THE BUILDING STONE
HERITAGE
OF
LEEDS

†FRANCIS G. DIMES
AND
MURRAY MITCHELL

with contributions by
JAMES NUNNEY
(sketches drawn by Vanessa Warnes
and maps by Jerry Hodgson)

LEEDS
THE LEEDS PHILOSOPHICAL AND LITERARY SOCIETY LTD
DECEMBER 1996

Proceedings of The Leeds Philosophical and Literary Society, Scientific Section.
Special Publication

NOTICES

1 — Applications for copies or sets of the Society's Publications should be made to the Honorary Secretary —
> The Leeds Philosophical and Literary Society,
> City Museum, Calverley Street, Leeds LS1 3AA

2 — Authors may receive, on request, eight offprints without charge. Additional copies may be obtained at cost price.

Editor Scientific Section

Dr H. M. PANTIN
Department of Earth Sciences
University of Leeds
Leeds LS2 9JT. England, UK

British Library Cataloguing-in-Publication Data:
a catalogue record for this book is available from the British Library.

ISBN 1 870737 10 5

Printed in Great Britain by W. S. Maney and Son Ltd Leeds

CONTENTS

LIST OF ILLUSTRATIONS

MAPS

PLATES

Between pages 52 and 53

DEDICATION

Frank Dimes worked on 'The Building Stone Heritage of Leeds' for a number of years, and throughout that time I received regular reports from him of the book's progress. He particularly enjoyed the time he spent discussing the finer points of stone work with his close friend and co-author Murray Mitchell on their many walks along the streets of Leeds — a city for which he had great affection.

Until he retired in 1980, Frank was the Curator of Building Stones at the Geological Museum in South Kensington, yet he was probably as well known to geologists, members of the stone fraternity, and students after his retirement as during his long and distinguished career.

He was a Liveryman of the Worshipful Company of Masons and a Freeman of the City of London, but most of all, Frank was a great educator. The contribution he made to the teaching of geology, and particularly the study of building stones, was immense. He was one of the longest standing extra-mural lecturers for the University of London, and also had a large and loyal following at his lectures and field trips presented for the adult education service at London's Natural History Museum.

Frank brought to this project a lifetime's experience of the nature and use of building stone, and the book was near completion at the time of his death on the 8 October 1995. How sad that he did not see the final published version.

At Murray's request *The Building Stone Heritage of Leeds* is dedicated to the memory of Frank Dimes and his lasting contributions to the building stones of Great Britain.

DR ALAN TIMMS
Head of Adult and Continuing Education
The Natural History Museum
London
March 1996

FOREWORD

The building fabric of a town reveals its history and determines its character; it is an integral part, perhaps the most important part, of its personality, the part that makes the greatest impact and most enduring impression on the visitor. The fabric is a record of small beginnings, of aspirations, of prosperity, of decline and of revival, an archive of changing personalities, technologies and economics.

When the building fabric is principally stone, there may be a quality to the town which is not easy to define, but which somehow makes it comfortable in its landscape; Aberdeen's granite, Bath's limestone, the slate of Blaenau Ffestiniog or the sandstone of Newcastle. Still other towns, first built of their native stone, later brought in new stones from other regions in response to fashion, and were enabled by canals and railways to develop new styles in materials not dictated by necessity. Of these last, Leeds is a prominent and striking example. To those with eyes to see, Leeds is full of a range of stone used in a splendid variety of ways which still holds it together and leaves an enduring impression of a city which survives the later, anonymous and unmemorable development. Bad planning and poor quality development are popularly blamed on economics; they may be more accurately attributed to ignorance of what is achievable and desirable, and to simple bad manners. No development of an historic town or city should be permitted without a prior intimacy with its character and its past. Out of time taken to look and learn comes appreciation, and with appreciation, respect.

With this in mind, this book has a very significant contribution to make to the past and future of Leeds. Familiar buildings take on new interest, and buildings never seen before, now demand a visit. Once visited or revisited with the expert guidance of the authors, the value and the pleasure of all these buildings is immeasurably enhanced.

That Frank Dimes should not live to see the publication of this book is a matter of considerable sorrow; but it is nevertheless a real pleasure and delight that so much of his authority, enthusiasm and enjoyment is still available through this text. Countless students, professionals, and enthusiastic amateurs have followed Frank's 'stonewalks' not just in Leeds, but in many cities and cathedrals. His contribution to the understanding and appreciation of building and decorative stone internationally is prodigious.

I was privileged to work and write with Frank Dimes many times over the past thirty years, and am delighted that, with his friend and co-author Murray Mitchell, he is still able to teach, and inspire interest, with some of the passion for his subject that he was never able to conceal and was always ready to share.

The Building Stone Heritage of Leeds will become an important reference work of real scholarship, but also a well-thumbed field manual which should be seen often on the streets of the city. It is a model for other works of this kind.

A work of this calibre will be of immense use to geologists, historians, architects, planners, and the interested public, a substantial authority and, it may be hoped, a defence against neglect, apathy and destruction.

PROFESSOR JOHN ASHURST RIBA EASA (Hons)

PREFACE

Leeds celebrated its 100 years of history as a City in 1993. This book looks back over the story of how it was built: a story here told in stone.

In the beginning the stone was locally quarried: cartage from any distance was expensive. With the spread first of the canals and then of the railways, a great and amazing variety of stone, initially from British localities, was drawn into the city. Nowadays the stones come from around the world; marbles from Italy, granites from Sweden, serpentinites from Greece, exotic rocks from South America and South Africa — all can be seen in Leeds.

This book attempts an historical approach, relating the stones used to the changing building styles. Five distinct periods may be distinguished in the growth of the present day city: early Georgian, mainly brick with sandstone dressings; late Georgian and early Victorian, the classic local sandstone age; late Victorian, the peak time for inventive changes in style and material; early twentieth century to modern, when cladding demanded different stones and techniques; and the post-1950s ferro-concrete age which overlaps with the modern stone-cladding style.

Leeds is indeed fortunate that some of the fascinating buildings from earlier times still stand amongst the jumble of modern commercial towers, the contrast being a vivid manifestation of the way Leeds has developed.

The more interesting and important buildings in the centre of Leeds have been grouped together into four walks which give the reader an oversight of the different periods. Each walk takes about two hours at a leisurely pace. Another group of significant buildings is described as 'Further Afield: Well worth a visit'. These are in outlying areas or do not fit conveniently into the routes taken by the four walks.

It is the buildings of stone that have survived. Of the stones, some such as the renowned granite from Shap on the edge of the Lake District are highly distinctive, but many others are more difficult to identify. The earliest stones used for building were the local sandstones, and much research was required to discover the details of their source. The major Victorian growth of Leeds was in fact dependant on the local geology; the two were inseparable.

Linstrum's 1969 account of the architectural history of Leeds has excellent illustrations, including photographs of many of the buildings described in the walks. His 1978 publication is a major work of reference for information about the architecture of West Yorkshire's buildings.

Surprisingly for a city of the size and importance of Leeds, the only previous account of its building stones was in 1940 by the late H. C. Versey, Professor of Geology at Leeds University, who led a number of city walks to demonstrate the use of stone for building.

Now, it is hoped that readers as they walk the streets with this book will sense the long building-stone history and heritage of Leeds, and its importance to the future of the City. We have inherited many fine buildings from previous generations and hold these in trust for the future.

MURRAY MITCHELL
Department of Earth Sciences
University of Leeds
March 1996

NOTE ADDED IN PROOF

A considerable amount of rebuilding and refurbishment is currently being carried out in Leeds, and readers should be aware that some of the buildings described in this book may soon be replaced or renamed.

The three major new buildings discussed in Walk 2 (Nos 22, 28, and 29), presently under construction, should be completed in 1997. The materials noted are those that the architects proposed to use. Other changes include the Schofield Centre (Chapter 5.12), renamed the Headrow Shopping Centre following the closure of the Schofields shop, which is now occupied by Lillywhites. The Bond Street Centre (Walk 4: 70 and 71) is being refurbished as the Leeds Shopping Plaza, and Maples (Chapter 5.14) is due to close before the end of 1996.

Major new developments not described in the book include The Royal Armouries, south of the River Aire, opened in early 1996; Harvey Nichols shop on the site of the Empire Theatre in Briggate, opening in October 1996; and a large extension to the Leeds General Infirmary, due to open in 1997.

14 October 1996

CHAPTER 1

History of Building Stones in Leeds

'You must like it very much or not at all'
wrote Dickens when he visited Leeds

(Dexter 1925, p. 231)

Works in stone are often the most enduring and, in the absence of the written word, the only evidence for the history of early activities. The use of stone enabled structures to survive so that something of the history and development of settlements can be studied. Where the stone came from and how it was used provides a great thread through time. Leeds has a long history, although little remains of the early buildings. Medieval growth owed its origins to the creation, in the early thirteenth century, of Briggate which became a cloth market of increasing importance, with long thin plots at right angles to the street. Although the layout of this stage of the history of Leeds can still be traced, no buildings survive. By the mid-seventeenth century Leeds was a major regional market based on the expanding cloth trade. In the early parts of the Industrial Revolution the prosperity of Leeds continued to be based on textile industries. During the late eighteenth-century woollen and flax mills flourished, to which were added the ever increasingly important foundries and engineering works. The combination of textile and engineering works was the basis of the rapid growth of Leeds in the Victorian period. Through this prosperous time the ready-made clothing industries blossomed, and with increased wealth, new banks and insurance offices opened. It is perhaps the great civic and commercial buildings which make Leeds primarily a Victorian city, with rich and varied structures providing some of the best uses of stone, particularly the local Yorkshire sandstones.

Geology played little part in the early history of Leeds, although Coal Measures sandstones from within the old township were available and were probably used for the few major buildings. However, the fortunate siting of Leeds on the edge of the exposed Yorkshire Coalfield later provided easily accessible and cheap sources of the coal and iron which were so important in the Industrial Revolution's growth of the town. As a condition of being allowed to run a wagon-way down to the River Aire in 1758, for example, the Middleton Colliery owners were required to supply coal to Leeds at a fixed price, thus ensuring that the city had an ample supply of cheap coal. The presence of good brick-making clays and many sandstone horizons both in the upper part of the Millstone Grit and in the Coal Measures was also of prime importance, providing vast supplies of excellent building material for the mushrooming mills, foundries and housing, as well as commercial and public buildings. The presence of the Aire valley passing through the heart of Leeds, with the river providing water power in the early days and later easy transport, was an equally vital feature in the town's history.

This account of the history of the use of stone for building in Leeds concentrates on the central area. An attempt is made to trace the changing trends brought on by the advances of technology and transport during the Industrial Revolution. The Victorian period was so important in the building stone history of Leeds that the surviving buildings from the years 1850 to 1911 are listed in the Appendix.

Georgian, and early to mid-Victorian buildings in Leeds were predominantly constructed from local bricks, and locally quarried sandstones. However, late-Victorian and Edwardian times saw several very important changes with increasing 'imports' by rail of sandstones from more distant Yorkshire quarries and of other constructional stone, especially Scottish granite. Much local red brick was also used, with sandstone dressings, terracotta and coloured glazed tiles ('Multicoloured Town' of Linstrum 1978, p. 22).

Two factors were of major importance to the changing scene in the twentieth century. First, there was the fundamental change in method of construction to steel-framed concrete buildings, which saw the end of the use of stone as a constructional load-bearing material, and started the flood of exotic cladding stones from world wide sources that has been responsible for so much of the texture and colour of modern Leeds. Secondly, there was the Leeds Council's decision to use white Portland Stone for the scheme to widen The Headrow.

Study of the bricks which are extensively used in Leeds is outside the scope of the present work.

Pre-Norman Leeds

Nothing is known of any settlement at Leeds before the Romans, although it is possible that there may have been a Roman station near Leeds at the first place that the River Aire could be forded above the swamps of the Vale of York. However, there is no direct evidence for this, and the early history of the area is obscure. The earliest evidence for Leeds is provided by a reference in the Venerable Bede's work (A.D. 731) to the 'regio of Loidis' (the old form of the city's name) which may have been a royal centre in the seventh century (Plummer 1896). In addition, the remains of at least five Anglian sculptured crosses have been found (McGuire and Clark 1987). It was with great good fortune that fragments of these crosses are preserved, because it was only during the demolition of the old Parish Church of St Peter in 1838 that the carved stones were recognized amongst the fabric of the old church and their value appreciated (see Chapter 5:21).

The Domesday Survey of 1086 confirms that there was a pre-Norman settlement at Leeds — with cottages, a priest, a church and a mill. The church (Moore 1877; Chapter 5:20) would have been a simple Anglo-Saxon building and the focus for a small agricultural village on raised ground above an Aire valley crossing point.

It is interesting to speculate that if Leeds had remained as a small village, this simple Anglo-Saxon church might have survived. However, continuing growth led to the need for ever bigger churches, so this early church with those from Norman times and the fourteenth century were each in turn swept aside until the present church was built in an attempt to satisfy the needs of the early Victorian parish.

Norman Leeds

In Norman times the settlement of Leeds continued to be centred on the Church of St Peter, which was probably repaired or rebuilt during this period, because much Norman stonework was re-used in the later fourteenth-century church (see 5:20).

Two important outlying sites provide valuable clues to the history of the use of building stones at this time. The vast but simple and relatively undecorated Cistercian Kirkstall Abbey was built in the twenty years or so following its foundation in 1152 (see 5:2). The remote and isolated nature of this part of the Aire valley in Norman times was much in keeping with the strict Cistercian rules for the avoidance of worldly distractions. The other building is the Church of St John the Baptist at Adel (Figure 1), about 3 miles north-north-east of Kirkstall. This small simple structure was built in the second half of the twelfth century at about the same time as Kirkstall Abbey, but is in marked contrast to the massive Abbey. The outstanding features of Adel church are two fine Norman arches, one over the south door and the other forming the chancel arch (see 5:3). The presence of this fine example of Norman architecture at Adel, close to the line of the Roman road which is known to have crossed the moorland a little way to the north, suggests that there may have been an important early settlement in the area.

Late Medieval to Seventeenth-century Leeds

The late medieval town grew around three centres, the parish church in the east with Kirkgate as its main street, the manor house and mill in the west, and Briggate leading north from the Aire. The Scarborough Hotel now stands on the site of the old manor house in Bishopgate. The mill, such an economically important part of the manor, was on the head race in the grounds between the present railway-station site and the foot of Briggate. The Church of St Peter of this time continued to be the dominant building and saw periods of repair and rebuilding first in the fourteenth century, and later in the early sixteenth century after about 1500, when much of the church was destroyed by fire (see 5:20).

Briggate ('the road to the bridge') which became the nucleus of the medieval market town of Leeds dates from 1207, when the Lord of the Manor granted the settlement its first borough charter and deliberately established a 'new town' to the west of the old village centred on St Peter's. Briggate and about 30 long narrow burgage plots, at right angles to and on both sides of the new street running north from the Aire, formed the basis of this new development. The

FIGURE 1.   Church of St John the Baptist, Adel

first bridge probably dates from the fourteenth century (about 1372). Briggate and Leeds Bridge, as it was known, became the centre for the cloth market, held on Tuesday and Saturday mornings, upon which the medieval prosperity of Leeds was founded.

The houses of this old town were of mud and timber, with a few 'of the richer sort of Inhabitants' having houses of stone (Heap 1988), and although many of the late sixteenth-century picturesque gabled houses and old inns survived well into the nineteenth century, the only remaining timber-framed house, dating from about 1600, may be seen in Lambert's Yard off the east side of Lower Briggate. The distinctive layout of the medieval town can be clearly seen from the early maps of Leeds. It had changed little by the time of Cossin's 'New and Exact Plan' of 1725, and even Jeffery's 'Plan' of 1770. The plots running off Briggate can be traced today in the form of the old Inn Yards, alleyways and shopping arcades which are such an essential and distinctive characteristic of central Leeds.

A feature of the Briggate-based old town was the erection of Bar Stones. These were not parts of any form of fortified gateway, but marked the boundary between the medieval manorial borough (Leeds Town) and the surrounding agricultural land (or Leeds Main Riding). Certain privileges were enjoyed by the Town inhabitants who paid low tithes, had letters delivered free to dwellers within the bars and were exempt from jury service at York Assizes (Sprittles 1969, p. 89).

The age of the Bar Stones is not known, but the Burley Bar Stone was referred to by Thoresby in 1715. This and the York Bar are marked on Cossin's 1725 map. It is probable that they are much older than this, and may be some of the oldest remaining evidence of medieval Leeds stonework (Beresford 1988, p. 7; see 5:22).

The Church of St John in New Briggate was started in 1631 and consecrated in 1634. Endowed by John Harrison, a leading Leeds citizen of his day, it is the oldest surviving church in central Leeds. Built partly to cater for the needs of the growing population of the parish, it is of great historical interest because early seventeenth-century churches are uncommon. The site was in fields then outside the town's boundary on a rise once known as the 'town cliff' (see 5:13). Fine merchant houses were a feature of this period (Cossins 1725 Plan), one of the remaining examples now being Nash's Fish and Chip restaurant in Merrion Street (Map 2). The original south-facing frontage of this building is of a fine-grained sandstone, now unfortunately painted over, and the side facing Merrion Street has a mock-tudor façade.

The Moot Hall which stood in the middle of Briggate, extending approximately from the present junction with Commercial Street to the County Arcade, was built in 1618, rebuilt in 1710, and demolished in 1825. The statue of Queen Anne which adorned its front is preserved in the City Art Gallery. The statue is very dirty and badly needs cleaning. Through the grime it appears to be Carrara Marble and almost certainly First Statuary quality.

Georgian Leeds

Many fine Georgian buildings including the Infirmary (1768–71) and the Coloured Cloth Hall (1756–58), have been swept away by redevelopment (Grady 1989). However, the frontage of the 1775 White Cloth Hall in The Calls, replacing the 1755 Meadow Lane Hall, has been preserved. Harewood House (1759–71) is worthy of mention (see 5:10) because its successful construction probably led to the development of Rawden Hill Quarry west of Harewood, which supplied one of the classic early Victorian Leeds sandstones.

The most important remaining eighteenth-century addition to the Leeds scene is Holy Trinity Church in Boar Lane. Built between 1722 and 1726, it was the third church in Leeds after St Peter's and St John's (see 5:15). Boar Lane was a narrow cramped medieval street at the time Holy Trinity was opened, but was a fashionable place for merchants to live. It was widened to its present layout after 1866.

B

Several of the fine public buildings which once graced Leeds in the early part of the nineteenth century were constructed of locally quarried sandstone. Both the County Court (1811–13) and the Philosophical Hall (1819–22) in Park Row, and the early Victorian Stock Exchange (1846–47) on the corner of Albion Street and Albion Place, were built of Harehills Stone from the quarries in Harehills and Gipton Wood, about 2 miles north-east of Leeds. These quarries (see Table 2) worked the Elland Flags (Coal Measures). Harehills Stone was 'until about 1856, almost the only stone of its kind employed by local architects', and had a reputation in Leeds comparable to that of Bath and Portland in London, and Craigleith in Edinburgh. It was the nearest fine-grained sandstone available to Leeds, the easiest to work and proved the most durable of all the finer stones that could be conveniently used without great expense (Alfred Waterhouse, in *Dictionary of Architecture* about 1863, vol. 4, p. H22). The grand Ionic Commercial Building (1826–29) which stood on the City Square–Boar Lane corner was also built of Elland Flags, but from Park Spring Quarries, Bramley, $3\frac{1}{2}$ miles west of Leeds. This stone although 'beautiful in appearance' did not prove to be as durable as Harehills Stone and crumbled badly (*Dictionary of Architecture* 1881, vol. 6, p. P51).

The early days of the Industrial Revolution in late Georgian times saw the beginnings of the rapid growth in both size and prosperity of Leeds. Comparison of Jeffrey's 1770 map of basically medieval Leeds with Netlam and Francis Giles 1815 map shows the expansion of both the West End and East End which has been described in detail by Beresford (1988). In the west, Park Row (1768), South Parade (1776), East Parade (1779), the Park Square estate (1788) and Albion Street (1792) all date from this time and were originally laid out mainly as residential areas with large houses on broad plots. Use of locally-made bricks played a major part in these new developments, with the clay commonly coming from the foundation excavations, and the bricks burnt in small brickworks adjacent to the sites (Beresford 1988, p. 154).

A few Georgian buildings have survived in the centre of Leeds. On the north side of Albion Place near the Albion Street junction, a late eighteenth-century house built of brick with fine-grained, buff-coloured sandstone dressings is a relic of this once fashionable residential area (Walk 4:85, Figure 2). The Leeds Library (1808) on the north side of Commercial Street, between Albion Street and Lands Lane, has a stone frontage which has been painted over. Designed by T. Johnson, it is a long-established subscription library. Another late Georgian site is on the east side of the corner of Bank Street and Commercial Street. Built for the Union Bank in 1813, it later housed Williams, Brown and Company's Bank before its move to Greek Street Chambers (Walk 2:33) in Park Row. The frontage was remodelled in the 1850s and the stonework is now painted over.

The first effects of the dramatic changes brought about by the Industrial Revolution started to be felt in the latter part of the eighteenth century. Before these changes, the long-established skills of working in stone had seen few changes. All work was carried out by hand. Mill Hill Chapel built in 1848

FIGURE 2.   No. 1 Albion Place

(Walk 3:39) is one of the last examples in Leeds of these craft skills. Commonly the most expensive part of building works was the transport of the stone from quarry to site. As a result, large numbers of relatively small quarries were opened as close as possible to the areas of building, producing the many delf (or quarry) 'oles of Yorkshire. The Leeds and Liverpool Canal, started in 1770 but not completed until 1816, had a great impact on the transport of building materials as well as all bulky goods. The earliest evidence of this was the arrival of vast quantities of purple-coloured North Wales slate, which soon became the dominant roofing material in Leeds, ending the use of heavy slabs (thackstones) of local fine-grained flaggy sandstone.

Early Victorian Leeds (to about 1860)

The stone working industries were generally conservative, dependant on a large labour force of highly skilled craftsmen, and were slow to take advantage of Industrial Revolution changes. However, steam power was harnessed for

MOORLANDS HOUSE

lifting and moving stone within quarries. Although the cutting of stone was soon mechanized, the quarrying of the blocks and much of the dressing and finishing of the stone continued to be done by hand well into the twentieth century. Gradually work became concentrated on the bigger quarries producing the better quality stones. As they were mechanized and enlarged, large numbers of small local quarries were abandoned. Direct access to a railway became essential for a quarry to prosper, and with the country's rapidly spreading rail network, granites (initially from Scotland) started to be used after about 1860.

The classic sandstone quarries close to Leeds during the early Victorian period include those at Bramley Fall, Harehills, Horsforth, Meanwood, Weetwood, Potternewton, Rawden Hill near Harewood and Pool Bank. Of these, only Pool Bank, with good reserves of high quality stone and with access to the Leeds and Thirsk Railway at Arthington, continued to supply building stone to Leeds after the 1860s.

There is relatively little that survives of early Victorian Leeds but Moorlands House in Albion Street (1852–55: Walk 4:69) is a fine example. It was only after about the 1820s that prosperity led to the construction of many splendid public buildings, particularly the banks and commercial offices which are a feature of Leeds. These buildings mark one of the high points for the activities of the sandstone quarries in Yorkshire. The Appendix lists the surviving post-1850 Victorian and Edwardian buildings, many of which are described in the illustrated walks (Chapters 4 and 5).

Factors other than transport may have hastened the decline of the local Leeds sandstone quarries. Reserves may have been exhausted as quarries extended to the edge of their areas; many quarries were worked into the sides of valleys and increasing thickness of overburden may have become a problem; and the rapid mid-Victorian spread of urban housing may have put pressure on the value of land near the centre of town, removing the possibility of quarry extensions.

Late Victorian Leeds (from about 1860)

Many of the buildings from 1850 to the 1890s were built of sandstones from Yorkshire. The typical use was to have fine- to medium-grained buff-coloured sandstones for the main walls, because these were easier to work and to carve in fine detail, resting on a plinth of coarse-grained, massive, weather-resistant blocks of Millstone Grit, usually the Rough Rock (see Table 2). As Leeds became the chief financial centre of the West Riding, the number of banks increased from three to twelve between 1859 and 1869 (Douglas and Powell 1988, p. 2). Initially the new banks made use of existing properties, but as they prospered, purpose-built offices in a wide range of architectural styles soon appeared, particularly in the 1890s, to grace the business area centred on Park Row.

Three significant changes took place in late Victorian Leeds. The first change resulted directly from the spread of railways, which made transport easier and cheaper so that the requirement to quarry stone from as near to the building site as possible was no longer essential. The local quarries used in early Victorian times ceased working and from the early 1860s sandstone was brought to Leeds from a surprising range of more distant West Riding quarries. The quality of the stone may have become the most important requirement, and the quarries with good rail links that continued in production expanded greatly in the years that followed. Late Victorian building in Leeds used sandstone from Crosland Moor, Huddersfield, Ringby at Halifax, Haworth, Bolton Woods near Bradford, Idle, Eccleshill, Burley-in-Wharfedale, the Horsforth area and Morley Moor. Granites, mainly from Scotland, were first used in 1862–63 (again as a result of the spread of railways), commonly to decorate entrances. An important feature of the time was the use of monolithic columns of Peterhead and of Aberdeen granites. Use of British granite was relatively minor until 1898, when the entire ground floor of Greek Street Chambers (Walk 2:33) was built of Scottish granites.

The other two late Victorian changes involved the use of different materials, and as Linstrum (1978, p. 22) noted, Leeds became a 'Multicoloured Town'. The first change saw red brick combined with sandstone dressings become an increasingly prominent and characteristic style. The second change, from about 1878, saw the introduction of terracotta and a range of Burmantofts Faience adding brighter colours to the scene. These changes led to a dramatic decline in the use of Yorkshire sandstones. The trade journals of the time have many articles about the comparative merits and costs of stone, brick and ceramic tiles. It is clear that Leeds was fortunate to have abundant supplies of clays from the Coal Measures available locally; their mineralogy means that these clays fire to make very resistant high-quality bricks. The removal of the tax on bricks in the 1850s and the early mechanization of their manufacture made bricks a competitive source of building material. The General Infirmary (1863–67) is one of the earliest Victorian uses of red brick with sandstone dressing (5:6). There are many other fine examples from the 1890s with the City of Leeds School (1889; Walk 1:9), the Medical School (1893–94; 5:4:6) and the frontage of Oxford Place Methodist Chapel (1896–1903; Walk 1:2) being typical.

A dramatic development was the introduction of terracotta from 1878 and of Burmantofts Faience from 1894. Both of these materials gave a new look to the streets of Leeds. The Burmantofts works in east Leeds was founded in 1842 and, at first, supplied coal, bricks and sanitary pipes from Rock Colliery. A change of management in 1879 led to rapid growth of the Burmantofts factory. In addition, the clay from the area was found to be suitable for the production of terracotta and decorative tiles. It was discovered that if the clay was fired at a very high temperature and glazed, it made a durable architectural material which was given the name Burmantofts Faience. This new building material had the advantage of eliminating dirt and weathering, needing only to be washed to be as good as new. It also added a wide range of colours. The Burmantofts works at this time also produced brightly coloured pottery. A late development at Burmantofts, after 1900, was a new kind of terracotta which was grey-white in colour and called Burmantofts Marmo Faience. The main usages of Burmantofts materials are listed in the Appendix and the history of the works is given in 'Burmantofts Pottery Catalogue' published in 1984 by Bradford Art Galleries and Museums and Leeds City Museum. In the 1920s the works occupied a sixteen acre site with ninety operating kilns. It must have had a dramatic effect on the east Leeds scene. The works closed in 1957. One of its last contracts was to supply tiles for the Empire Swimming Pool, Cardiff, opened in 1958.

Many of the late Victorian office buildings were decorated or carved with the name of the company responsible for the original construction. This is an interesting reflection on the great sense of continuity and permanence that was such a dominant feature of this prosperous time.

Early Twentieth-Century Leeds (Edwardian)

The use of sandstones continued to decline in the early part of the twentieth century. Goodbard House (Walk 3:56) built in 1905 was one of the last of the major buildings in Yorkshire sandstone. Another significant building is Pearl Chambers (Walk 3:67) built in 1911. It was constructed entirely of stone from outside the Leeds area, with Aberdeen granite for the ground floor, and one of the first large scale uses in Leeds of white Portland Stone from Dorset for the upper floors (*Building News* 1909, p. 905).

Post-1920s to Present Date

The period from 1911 to 1930 saw very little new major building in central Leeds. The Yorkshire sandstone quarries and their workers appear to have suffered badly. They must have faced serious competition from bricks, terracotta and stone brought in by rail from other parts of the country, and the skilled work force declined, perhaps with a drift to better-paid engineering work. Capital for developing the quarries reduced, particularly through the First World War and the following depressed times, with few orders for new buildings. The sandstone quarries may, therefore, have become less competitive. The decline was clearly a complex and serious problem. The prosperous years in late Victorian times were never repeated until perhaps very recently, and then in fewer but much larger operations.

The most important change in modern building techniques was the introduction of steel frames and reinforced concrete to carry the weight of the structure, with stone cladding purely to resist weathering and to improve appearance. This method of construction has been used exclusively through much of the twentieth century. It saw the end of the use of stone as a load-bearing material and a change to the need for stone that could be cut into relatively thin sheets for cladding. This change led to the introduction into Leeds of a great range of new colours and textures, with many stones being imported from world-wide sources. Attempts were also made to use concrete panels to face modern buildings. In some cases, crushed-granite aggregate was used for the facing panels in an attempt to improve the appearance of the concrete; others have exposed-aggregate panels, where concrete is washed off the outer face of the slabs before it sets to leave a rough stone finish — the texture of which depends on the pebbles used in the aggregate. Stone cladding and various concrete finishes are a feature of all the post-1950s new commercial buildings, and local sandstones have also been used to face some of the new developments, leading to a revival for some stone quarries in the Leeds area. The 1977 Bond Street Centre (Walk 4:70) was the first building for 70 years to have used local sandstones; other examples are Cloth Hall Court in Infirmary Street (1980; Walk 3:58), Kings Court (1990; Walk 3:49), and the 1980–82 Henry Moore Sculpture Gallery extension to the Art Gallery (Walk 1:16).

In May 1924 the Leeds Council made a decision which was to have a major effect on the present day City. Plans were approved for widening The Headrow which involved demolishing the north side of the street from Cookridge Street to Eastgate. The unified redevelopment scheme used red, sand-stock bricks, Delabole roofing slate and white Portland Stone which was chosen to resist the soot blackening that affected local sandstone. This must, therefore, have been a conscious attempt to improve the Leeds scene, but was a serious blow to the depressed local sandstone industries. Permanent House (1930) on the corner of Cookridge Street was the first building of this scheme to be completed (see Walk 1:14; Heap 1990). Through the 1930s, Portland Stone continued to be used for most of the new public and commercial buildings. This characteristic white oolitic limestone makes a major contribution to the present face of central Leeds.

Decorative cladding is also a feature of shop fronts and, because of the relatively small quantities required, a great range of stones has been used. Many unusual rock types have been employed, making this aspect of the building-stone history of Leeds a source of much interest.

Modern buildings also have attempted to keep alive the distinctive 'Multicoloured Leeds' style of construction. Red brick often predominates the facings, with sandstone, reconstituted stone, or buff-coloured bricks forming the ornamental dressings.

A remarkable range of stone claddings continues to be used on the major commercial developments in Leeds, but a change has taken place in the last few years in the materials used for the shop fronts. Considerable renovation has been carried out in the shopping areas and arcades, with the intention of improving the appearance of central Leeds. However, as a result presumably of the present depressed times, very little new stone is being used. In fact, several notable examples of stone cladding fitted during more affluent times have been swept away in recent works, to be replaced by plastic sheeting or painted woodwork. It may be that the heyday for the use of decorative stone cladding for shop fronts has passed (dare one say it is hoped only temporarily?), so the present attempt to record some of the best examples in Leeds is timely.

CHAPTER 2
The Underlying Rocks

The geology and topography of the area played a crucial role in the economic rise of Leeds during the industrial revolution. The early prominence of the city as a manufacturing centre owed much to the availability of ample supplies of relatively cheap coal, and to the River Aire which provided both water power and a means of transport for bulky loads.

Geological time is divided into a number of periods or systems, during each of which a characteristic set of rocks was laid down. The periods are listed in Table 1. Leeds is situated on the eastern slopes of the Pennine Chain at the northern end of the exposed part of the Yorkshire Coalfield, and is underlain by rocks of Carboniferous age. The Carboniferous Period, which supplied much of the local stone used in the building of Leeds, is subdivided into three parts.

The lower division is the Carboniferous Limestone, which forms the splendid karst scenery of the Yorkshire Dales. Valuable building stones occur within this division, but their outcrops were too far distant from the city to be used in early times. The middle division is the Millstone Grit. This forms the sweeping, heather-covered gritstone moorlands of the Pennines and is made up mainly of medium- and coarse-grained sandstones. The upper division is the Coal Measures, which consists of horizons of fine-grained sandstone with much shale (some of which was fired to make excellent bricks), valuable deposits of ironstone and fireclay, and long-exploited coal seams. The boundary between the Millstone Grit and the Coal Measures passes through northern Leeds, so the rocks of both are readily available for use as building stone in Leeds (see Map 1).

Fortunately for Leeds, both the Millstone Grit and the Coal Measures contain many layers of sandstone which yield high-quality building stone. As stated earlier, until transport became easier and cheaper in the mid-nineteenth century, hundreds of quarries, many quite small, were opened in these sandstones to supply stone for local building needs. A few of these quarries were later developed on a much greater scale, and produced stone for nationwide as well as for local use.

The sandstones of both the Millstone Grit and the Coal Measures were deposited in the channels and in the outwash fans of a very large delta system. They commonly show the cross-bedding typical of deltaic sediments. Not surprisingly therefore, the sandstone horizons are highly variable in composition, thickness and lateral extent. Even within a single quarry the grain size and colour of a bed can vary greatly, so that it may be difficult to trace beds from one area to another. Building stone from an individual sandstone is thus difficult to distinguish from that of another, but generally the Millstone Grit rocks tend to be medium to coarse grained and those from the Coal Measures tend to be

TABLE 1:   The Order of Succession

ERA	PERIOD	CHARACTERISTIC ROCKS	
Caenozoic	Quaternary 2	Ice age and Interglacial deposits	
	Tertiary 65	Clay and sand	
Mesozoic	Cretaceous 144	Chalk, sandstone and clay	
	Jurassic 213	Limestone, sandstone and clay	
	Triassic 248	Sandstone	
Palaeozoic	Permian 286	Dolomitic limestone and sandstone	
	Carboniferous	Sandstone and shale	(Coal Measures)
		Sandstone and shale	(Millstone Grit)
	360	Limestone	(Carboniferous Limestone)
	Devonian 408	Sandstone and limestone	
	Silurian 438	Shale, limestone and sandstone	
	Ordovician 505	Shale, limestone and volcanic rocks	
	Cambrian 590	Shale and sandstone	
	Precambrian 4,800	Sedimentary, igneous and metamorphic rocks	

Figures are estimated ages in millions of years

fine grained. Colours are usually buff with variations from pale to dark and include orange hues.

Coarse-grained sandstones are sometimes referred to as 'Bramley Fall Stone' but this should really be regarded as a trade name. The famous original Bramley Fall Quarry worked the Rough Rock (Millstone Grit). Because of the expense of removing an increasing amount of overburden, this quarry ceased production in about 1839 (*The Quarry* 1900, p. 252). It had supplied very large blocks of coarse-grained sandstone used widely for engineering work, because of its great strength and resistant character. The Rough Rock is the highest sandstone of the Millstone Grit (see Table 2) and was quarried from many places other than Bramley Fall. This sandstone sometimes contains abundant pebbles of quartz,

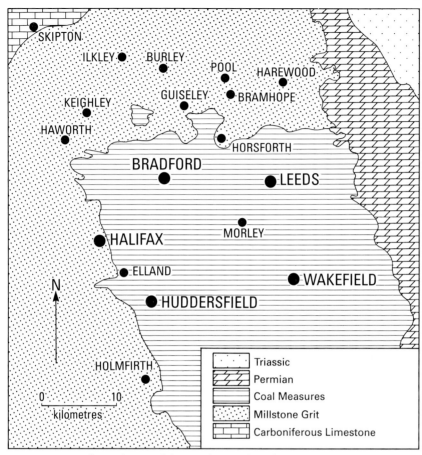

MAP 1. Geological map of the Leeds area; based on the British Geological
Survey Ten Mile Map

although this cannot be taken as a diagnostic feature. In this book, coarse-grained sandstones are described as coming from the Millstone Grit, but only as Rough Rock if the source quarry is known and the horizon confirmed. It should be noted that some of the sandstones recorded as from Bramley Fall would not have been from the original quarry but from other Rough Rock workings in the immediate area. One probable source for large quantities of high-quality Rough Rock building stone, for Leeds and sites further afield, may have been the large Whitehall Quarry at Hawksworth, south-east of Horsforth (Kendall and Wroot 1924, pp. 162, 667). This quarry was opened directly from the deep cutting excavated through the area when the Leeds and Thirsk Railway (the line from Leeds to Harrogate) was built in 1846 to 1849.

The same problem of stone names applies to the fine-grained sandstones from the Coal Measures to which the general term 'Elland Flags' is sometimes applied. However, Elland Flags is just one of the horizons of sandstone. It was extensively quarried and mined in former times, mainly for Yorkshire Flagstones for which this level had a national reputation. Offcuts from the trimming of flagstones were worked into roughly brick-sized blocks and extensively used for building, particularly in the Bradford area (Mr John Roberts, personal communication, 1993). Constructional stone, often called 'ashlar', also is quarried from the Elland Flags, although the blocks tend to be much smaller in size than those quarried from Millstone Grit sandstones.

The great majority of local Leeds sandstone quarries have long since been abandoned, many being filled in and grassed over. The details of these old quarries and the buildings that they supplied is beyond the scope of the present study; in fact, except in limited instances (see Godwin's 1984 fascinating account of mines in the Elland Flags), their history may never be written.

Only where evidence of quarry source is available can the sandstone horizon be confidently noted. In the absence of such records, Leeds sandstones can safely only be referred to as medium to coarse grained (taken to be from Millstone Grit) or fine grained (taken to be from Coal Measures). When used for building, the fine- and medium-grained sandstones can be intricately carved with fine detail, but the coarser-grained stones, particularly the Rough Rock, allow only simple bold carvings to be made.

Some long-standing West Yorkshire sandstone quarries still produce building stone, often with considerable outputs. The main active quarries, particularly those that are known to have supplied stone for use in Leeds, are noted in Table 2. A few of the more important disused quarries also are listed, and the stratigraphical horizon of the sandstone worked is indicated.

The basal beds of the Permian (Cadeby Formation, formerly known as the Lower Magnesian Limestone) crop out in north-east and east Leeds, but although these are the source of stone for the villages a little way to the east, surprisingly no records have been traced of their use in Leeds.

The geology of the region around Leeds was described in the following Geological Survey memoirs: for Bradford and Skipton (Stephens *et al.* 1953), for Huddersfield and Halifax (Wray *et al.* 1930), for Leeds (Edwards *et al.* 1950) and for Wakefield (Edwards *et al.* 1940). These works contain much valuable information about the building-stone quarries that were active at the time of the surveys in the 1920s and 1930s. Details in the present account about the position in the sequence of the quarried sandstones are based on these memoir accounts and their accompanying geological maps, with some revisions based on Burgess and Cooper (1980).

TABLE 2:   Carboniferous Sandstones and Quarries in Leeds Area

	SANDSTONE HORIZONS	SOME ACTIVE QUARRIES	SOME DISUSED QUARRIES
Coal Measures			
Middle C.M.	THORNHILL ROCK	Britannia Qy, Morley	Howley Park, Morley
Lower C.M.	ELLAND FLAGS	Southowram; Northowram; Ringby, Halifax	Eccleshill; Thornton; Woodhouse; Harehills; Park Spring, Bramley; Potternewton; Scott Hall; Fagley Qy, Bradford
	GAISBY ROCK	Bolton Woods, Bradford	Spinkwell, Bradford; Idle
	STANNINGLEY ROCK		Victoria, Stanningley
Millstone Grit			
'Rough Rock Group'	ROUGH ROCK	Crosland Hill, Huddersfield; Hawskworth, Guiseley	Bramley Fall; Newlay; Calverley Wood; Roo & Hawskworth, Horsforth; Weetwood; Meanwood
	ROUGH ROCK FLAGS	Hawksworth, Guiseley; Apperley Bridge, Rawdon; Buck Park, Cullingworth	
'Middle Grit Group'	HUDDERSFIELD WHITE ROCK	Hillhouse Edge, Huddersfield	
	GUISELEY GRIT	Guiseley Moor Top	Adel?
	BRANDON GRIT or PULE HILL GRIT	Clock Face, Scammonden; Naylor Hill, Haworth; Blackhill, Bramhope	West End, Haworth
	EAST CARLTON GRIT		
'Kinderscout Grit Group'	BRAMHOPE GRIT		
	{ADDINGHAM EDGE GRIT		Burley-in-Wharfedale
	{CALEY CRAGS GRIT		Pool Bank
'Middleton Grit Group'	UPPER FOLLIFOOT GRIT		
	LOWER FOLLIFOOT GRIT		Rawden Hill, Harewood

N.B.   Only the main sandstone horizons are shown. They are separated by shale which forms much of the sequence. The Gaisby Rock is referred to the Elland Flags by Waters *et al.* (1996).

Some of the nomenclature of these memoirs is now out of date. For example, the group names within the Millstone Grit are no longer used but are retained in Table 2 to allow cross-reference to these important works.

A revision of parts of the Leeds area (Lake *et al.* 1992) included up-to-date maps of the geology and of quarry sites. A similar resurvey of the Bradford area is in progress, and some results were presented in Waters *et al.* (1996).

CHAPTER 3

The Nature of Building Stone

Even a superficial look at the stones seen in the walk 'Shop Fronts Leeds' shows an apparently bewildering variety of stones used mostly decoratively — to attract the shopper. They differ in colour and texture; some are crystalline in nature; some contain fossils; yet despite this wide variety, any one of these stones may be placed into one of three big groups of rocks — the fundamental divisions used by geologists.

These divisions are determined by the characteristics of the stones; all stones with common characteristics are placed into the same group. Those character-istics depend on the way in which the stones were formed — their genesis.

There is now little doubt that the Earth was at one time in its early days a very hot molten ball. As it began to cool, the temperature of the surface decreased and a skin of rock — the crystallized state of the molten material — formed to become the crust of the Earth. That crust was violently disrupted through time but eventually it became thick enough to contain a still-liquid interior. The rocks of the early crust were crystallized, to greater or lesser degree depending on cooling conditions, from the molten rock material.

All rocks formed in that way, whether in the past or recently, are known as *Igneous Rocks*. They make up about 25 per cent of the earth's surface and may be very fine grained if cooled quickly at the surface, or coarse grained if cooled slowly within the crust. When igneous rocks are examined they are found to be an interlocking mass of mineral crystals. They can be classified by the chemical composition of the aggregate of minerals.

All rocks exposed on the Earth's surface are subjected to the forces of natural weathering — the rain, the wind, the sea, glacial action and the extremes of heat and cold, especially the freezing and thawing of water. The weathering process breaks down all rocks, either mechanically or chemically, and the breakdown products are carried away by water, ice or wind. It should be noted that rainwater is a weak acid and it is this that decomposes some minerals.

As the breakdown products are carried away they are sorted and concen-trated, and eventually deposited as a sediment, mostly on the sea floor, but sometimes in a lake or a desert basin. In time, these loose sediments are changed into 'solid' rocks; thus, for example, sands are converted into sandstones; and lime-mud into limestone.

These rocks are known as *Sedimentary Rocks*. Essentially they are granular, fragmented or detrital (clastic) in character. They are frequently layered or bedded, and often contain fossils, the remains of animals and plants that lived at the time these sediments were being laid down.

It may be noted here, that whereas igneous rocks may be made up of many different minerals, most sedimentary rocks are made up of just three — clay (mudstones and shales), quartz (sandstones) and calcite (limestones). Sedimentary rocks make up about 75 per cent of the Earth's surface.

Throughout geological time the rocks of the Earth's crust have had enormous forces exerted upon them. During mountain building periods, they have been squeezed, broken, fractured and faulted, and may have been heated to high temperatures. These forces change the original form of the rock — the process is known as metamorphism — the most noticeable change being one of recrystallization of the original mineral constituents (it must be noted that the chemistry remains the same — unless other matter has been introduced).

Sedimentary and igneous rocks which have been changed in this way are known as *Metamorphic Rocks*. A close look at them shows that their minerals are arranged in layers, either very finely as with slate, or rather more coarsely as with rocks known as schist and gneiss. Microscopic examination of marble (a metamorphosed limestone) shows it to be of roughly aligned calcite crystals.

Building on this basic classification of rocks — igneous, sedimentary, metamorphic — it is possible to construct detailed classifications for each group. These are discussed in Chapter 6.

The Use of Stone for Building

Before a stone is used for building, it is essential to know its nature, because that determines the way in which it may be used. For example, the very fine layering of the metamorphic rock slate enables it to be split into thin slabs which can be used on a roof.

But not all stones are suitable for building. It is evident, therefore, that other criteria now determine the use of any particular stone.

First, of course, the stone must be durable in human terms — no stone is durable in geological terms because all stones will weather through time. In the past, durability was found out by experience; nowadays, tests can indicate likely durability in given situations.

The durability cannot be judged from stone taken immediately from the quarry. These stones will contain 'quarry sap', groundwaters contained in the released block. In this saturated state most stones are easier to work than when the stone has dried out — the mason says that it has hardened. As there is no chemical change that can be detected in the stone, presumably the change is due to some physical process.

Secondly, a stone must be strong enough to resist the forces applied to it. Very few stones are structurally weak and most will support structures with little difficulty. Now that nearly all buildings are clad, rather than being built 'block on block', structural strength is of less importance.

Thirdly, stone should be attractive to look at. Highly decorative stones are used widely for shop fronts, but usually not for walls of buildings where they would be visually overpowering.

EXAMINING STONE.

Lastly, and probably most importantly, the stone should be available. Availability is not just a matter of getting the stone out of the quarry. Transport becomes of crucial importance.

As is seen in Chapter 1 on the History of Building Stones in Leeds, dozens of small local quarries formerly supplied stone for building in the City. As the canals, then the railways and later the roads spread across Great Britain, stone was brought from further and further away. Even so, the transport of stone was an expensive undertaking. Surviving records and accounts of some early medieval monastic buildings show that in those days the costs of carting exceeded the combined costs of all the rest of the quarrying, masonry and construction work. As late as the 1700s, when Wren was building his magnificent St Paul's Cathedral in London, the cost of transporting stone from the Isle of Portland exceeded the cost of purchasing the quarried blocks, even with the huge advantage of being able to bring the stone round by sea from Portland, where the quarries are on the cliff edge, and up the River Thames to London. Nowadays, stone is brought from almost anywhere around the world, a direct reflection of the ease of modern-day transport. With a comprehensive road network added to the efficiency of road transport, the relative cost of transporting stone has fallen dramatically. Today blocks of Portland Stone would cost only about one seventh more after cartage to London.

So, the development of Leeds has passed through an early sandstone building phase, the stone coming from local quarries, into a Victorian phase with a variety of stone from further afield being brought in by rail, until today when stone can be identified as coming from as far away as India, South Africa, Brazil, Canada, the USA and elsewhere.

Looking at Stone on a Building

A superficial look at many of the stones used for buildings in Leeds shows that they are dirty. Much — but by no means all — of this dirt may be removed by simply washing with plain water. The reader may find it to be of advantage to carry a damp sponge or cloth with which to wipe down the surface of the stone to be inspected. This technique also has the additional advantage of putting a temporary 'polish' on the stone, thus enhancing its features. This technique is not successful on stones which cannot initially be polished to any degree, such as oolitic limestones and sandstones. Care should be taken to explain what is happening to any puzzled and possibly irate shopkeepers.

Inspection of the surface of the stone is best carried out using a x10 lens. Binoculars are useful to inspect features on buildings at high level and, having twisted and turned through streets, roads and alleyways, a compass may be found useful to establish the facing directions of a façade.

CHAPTER 4
The Walks

The changing building styles, together with something of the variety of stones used, may be seen in the series of four walks described here.

Many of the best examples of building stones are found within the area roughly bounded by the Inner Ring Road, Boar Lane, East Parade and Vicar Lane. The four walks are conveniently made through this central part of Leeds (Map 2).

Walk 1:   'Civic Buildings' includes the main municipal buildings to the
            north of The Headrow (Map 3)

Walk 2:   'Commercial Buildings' (1) concentrates on Park Row (Map 4)

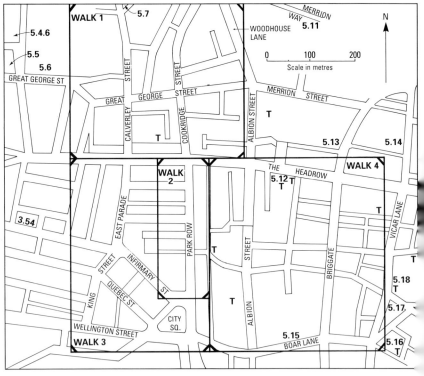

MAP 2.   Map of central Leeds, showing the areas covered by the four walks and
          some of the sites described in Chapter 5; Ts indicate Toilets

WARNING

Please take great care of the TRAFFIC if you are referring to this book while walking round the centre of Leeds.

Walk 3:   'Commercial Buildings' (2) covers the area around City Square and East Parade (Map 5)

Walk 4:   'Shop Fronts Leeds' with its great variety of exotic stones, many from abroad, takes in the area between Park Row and Vicar Lane (Map 6)

The map for each walk has numbers which locate the sites described and these numbers are noted in the text. Many of the buildings described have been 'listed' by the Department of National Heritage, as being of special architectural or historic interest, with the aim of ensuring their long-term survival. The Gradings (I, II* & II) of the 'LISTED BUILDINGS' are noted after the map reference numbers. For the comfort of the walker, public lavatories are indicated; but it should be remembered that most of these are open only during normal office hours!

Douglas and Powell (1988) described three Leeds architectural walks, and this has provided much valuable information about the history of the buildings in Leeds.

There are, however, many important buildings outside the area of these walks. These have been described in Chapter 5 as 'Further Afield: Well Worth a Visit' (Map 7). They show many features which are of interest historically, or use unusual stones. There are many fine industrial buildings in Leeds, particularly south of the River Aire, but this work has not been extended to include them.

WALK 1: Civic Buildings (Map 3)

The Civic Buildings walk starts at the TOWN HALL (1:1, Plate 1a). Asa Briggs (1961) gave a detailed account of the construction of this massive monument to Leeds civic pride which set out to be bigger and grander than the Town Halls of neighbouring Bradford, of Huddersfield or of Halifax. The Leeds gem of a Town Hall was built by Cuthbert Brodrick from 1853 and the opening ceremony 'amidst scenes of popular rejoicing' was performed before a great throng of people on the 7 September 1858 by Queen Victoria. At the time of its opening it was without its crowning tower, which was at first considered to be too costly; in mid-Victorian times, for even as major a construction as this, economy was an ever-present consideration. Briggs (loc. cit., p. 301) listed the local stone used as having been quarried at Bramley Fall, Calverley Wood, Pool Bank and Rawdon [sic] Hill, here thought to refer to the quarry at Rawden Hill near Harewood. Rawden Hill Quarry was worked by Trickett and Perkin from 1824 to 1859, and records in the Leeds City Archives show that stone from here was used in the building of the Town Hall. The quarry was experiencing difficulties

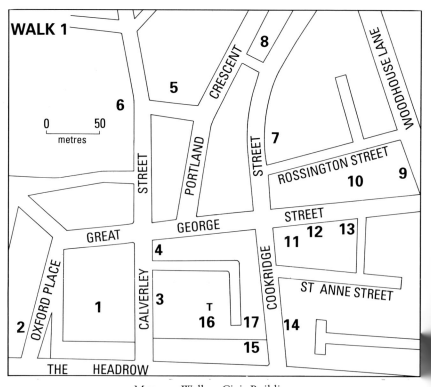

MAP 3.   Walk 1: Civic Buildings

with the quality of stone in the years before it closed (Briggs loc. cit., p. 285). Rawdon Hill Quarry would have been too small to have been a major source of stone for Leeds. Bramley Fall and Calverley Wood quarries yielded the coarse-grained, pebbly sandstone of the Rough Rock (Millstone Grit) which is used for the massive basal blocks. Many of these are boldly carved in vermiculated rustication; the blocks below the four lamp standards are highly individualistic in style. Pool Bank worked the Caley Crags Grit, and Rawden Hill the Lower Follifoot Grit (both Millstone Grit). The large blocks of stone used for the south colonnade are recorded as from Darley Dale (Stancliffe Quarry) near Matlock in Derbyshire, where the Ashover Grit (Millstone Grit) is still quarried. The remarkable columns of the south front appear to be straight sided, but in fact they bulge slightly. The diameter increases slightly up their height before narrowing towards the top. The change in diameter may be as much as $\frac{1}{8}$th of an inch in one foot. This is an architectural device known as entasis which ensures that when seen from a distance the columns seem to be straight, and is a feature that can be seen in many of the columns in Leeds. There is also a reference (Irwin and Branson *in* Handbook of the Old Leeds Exhibition 1926, p. 262) to the use of Bolton Woods Stone, Gaisby Rock (Coal Measures), from Bradford, in the Town Hall.

The four lions ornamenting the front steps were added in 1867 and are noted by Briggs as an 'improvisation'. They were carved by sculptor Noble in Portland Stone, a white-coloured limestone, and have weathered badly, undoubtedly because of the heavily-polluted atmosphere of Victorian Leeds. Each lion is carved out of two pieces of stone with marked but similar zig-zag joints between

VW   TOWN HALL LION

the blocks. The lion to the west of the colonnade contains a large chert nodule. One lion has lost most of his facial detail and another appears to have lost his tail! The decay of the sandstone plinths under the limestone lions should also be noted (see Chapter 6). Briggs (loc. cit., p. 301) referred to the 'black lions' of Leeds Town Hall, indicating that they had a full coating of soot before cleaning!

The sculptured frieze above the main entrance is by John Thomas (one of the sculptors of the House of Commons), and depicts figures representing poetry, music, industry, fine arts and science receiving inspiration from Leeds (Broadhead 1981, p. 46).

Before leaving the Town Hall steps, it is worth noting OXFORD PLACE METHODIST CHAPEL (2:11, Plate 1a) which was built in 1835 as a plain brick building. The frontage was redesigned by G. F. Danby and W. H. Thorp in 1896–1903, and is a fine example of the Multicoloured Leeds use of local red pressed brick with sandstone dressings. The sandstone came from Morley Moor Quarries near Leeds (*Builder* 1904, p. 637) where the Thornhill Rock (Middle Coal Measures) has long been worked.

On the east side of Calverley Street stands the City Museum and Library, parts of the MUNICIPAL BUILDINGS (3:11*, Figure 3) constructed between 1876 and 1884 of fine-grained sandstones resting on coarse-grained basal blocks.

FIGURE 3.   Municipal Buildings

This building was designed by George Corson, and the *Building News* (1877, p. 36) noted that stone from Bolton Woods Quarry, Bradford, Gaisby Rock (Coal Measures) was used for the superstructure. Shap granite, with its distinctive large pink feldspar crystals, has been used for the entrance steps and because this stone becomes polished and slippery when worn, particularly by leather-soled shoes, it has been scoured to make it safe. The Calverley Street doorway has four monolithic Peterhead granite columns and leads to an entrance hall decorated with Caen Stone (a limestone from Normandy) for the walls, Peterhead and Rubislaw granite pillars on the ground floor, Devonshire marble for the first floor pillars and Hopton Wood Stone (Carboniferous Limestone), from near Matlock in Derbyshire for the stairway balustrades (*Builder* 1884, pp. 256, 305).

Walking away from The Headrow, the next site is the SCHOOL BOARD BUILDING (4:II*), also designed by Corson in 1878–81. Until recently it was in very poor condition. Water and frost damage had occurred at the base of the Pool Bank Stone, Caley Crags Grit (Millstone Grit) used for the superstructure, where it rests on the coarser-grained base of stone from Burley-in-Wharfedale, Addingham Edge Grit (Millstone Grit); (*Building News* 1881, p. 459). Major refurbishment (1994–95) of this splendid building, now known as CIVIC COURT, has taken place. Some of the stone work of the upper floors has been repaired using sandstone blocks from Stoke Hall Quarry, Grindleford (near Sheffield) in North Derbyshire, where the Lower Kinderscout Grit (Millstone Grit) is worked. Repairs to the basal storey used the slightly coarser-grained sandstone from Stanton Moor (Peak Moor Quarry), Stanton-in-the-Peak near Matlock, south-east Derbyshire, where the Ashover Grit (Millstone Grit), is quarried. It should be noted, however, that part of the repair, including most of the parapet above the balustrade immediately below the ground-floor windows on the north side, is 'plastic (mortar) repair'.

The gutters at the south end of Calverley Street are lined with blue-grey Scoria engineering blocks which are made from iron-furnace slag. There are several other examples of this interesting material in the Leeds streets.

Crossing Great George Street, the white CIVIC HALL (5:II, see Cover) by E. V. Harris stands to the north. It was built in the early 1930s with money from the Government's 'Unemployed Grants Committee', ninety per cent of the workforce coming from the local Unemployment Registers. The building was opened by King George V in 1933. Portland Stone was used. The reasons why this stone was used widely in Leeds through the 1930s are discussed later when describing Permanent House (Walk 1:14). Some blocks are particularly shelly and the extent to which shell material stands out from the surface of the stone gives some indication of the rate of weathering that has occurred since construction. The Civic Hall has a fine Cumbrian or Lakeland green slate roof (Borrowdale Volcanic Group ashes). The steps and paving in front of the main entrance were relaid in early 1994, using new blocks and slabs of Portland Stone. The building was cleaned in 1994–95.

The BROTHERTON WING (6) of the Leeds Infirmary, across the road on the west side of Calverley Street, is also built of Portland Stone, and where rainwater has washed off the window sills and run down the stone work, the clean stripes are typical of a feature known as 'Portland Stone moustaches'! Where the surface is not washed by rain, Portland Stone weathers to a pale-buff colour due to sulphation (see Chapter 6) and also becomes soot blackened.

To the east of the Civic Hall, the CIVIC THEATRE (7:11*, Figure 4), formerly the Leeds Institute, now houses the College of Music. It was built by Brodrick in 1865–68 for the Leeds Mechanics' Institute when their original 1842 site in South Parade became too small for its needs. The building was known as the 'Albert Hall' in late Victorian times. Coarse-grained sandstone containing quartz pebbles, and showing evidence of large-scale cross-bedding, was used for the whole building. The basement is built of large, smooth-faced, deeply-incised rusticated blocks. The stones were hand worked and some are carved into simple but bold features.

This sandstone came from Roo Quarry, Horsforth, situated at the southern end of the strip of ground between Long Row and Bachelor Lane, which worked the Rough Rock (Millstone Grit). The long-disused quarry is now filled in and built over (Mr R. A. Rawson, former quarry owner, of Long Row Horsforth, personal communication, 1993). The paving in front of the Civic Theatre is a fine example of the use of Yorkshire Flagstones from the Elland Flags (Coal Measures).

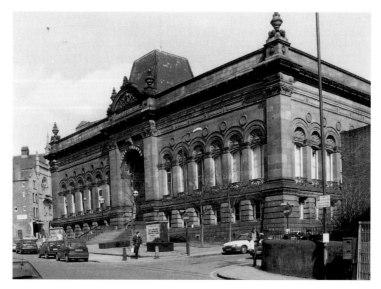

FIGURE 4.   The Civic Theatre, the former Mechanics' Institute, with the Coliseum partly seen on the left

The COLISEUM (8, Figure 4) further up Cookridge Street, built by William Bakewell as a theatre in 1885, has a frontage (topped by a statue of Britannia) made of fine-grained, buff-coloured sandstone from Howley Park Quarry, Morley (Watson 1911, p. 132) from which the Thornhill Rock (Middle Coal Measures) was quarried. The fine detail in which it has been possible to carve this sandstone, particularly the arch over the original main entrance, is in marked contrast to the simple, but bold carving which was all that was possible with the coarse-grained sandstone used for the Civic Theatre.

Turning south and passing the Civic Theatre, there are two more examples of Multicoloured Leeds on the south side of Rossington Street, with high quality red brick and sandstone dressings. At the top of the Street, the former CITY OF LEEDS SCHOOL (9:II), now Council offices, facing onto Woodhouse Lane, was built in 1889. It was one of the earliest purpose-built higher-grade schools in Britain and used coarse-grained Rough Rock (Millstone Grit), which again allowed only bold carving. The nearer building, the former PUPIL TEACHERS' CENTRE (10), built in 1900, uses fine-grained Coal Measures sandstone which is carved with more detail.

Continuing to the south, ST ANNE'S ROMAN CATHOLIC CATHEDRAL (11:II*, Plate 1b) was built between 1902 and 1904 on its present site at the corner of Great George Street and Cookridge Street, the architects being J. H. Eastwood and S. K. Greenslade. It replaced the 1838 building, demolished for street widening, that stood in the middle of the present Cookridge Street where it meets The Headrow.

The main walling is a coarse-grained, cross-bedded sandstone with conspicuous quartz pebbles. Eastwood (*Builder* 1901, p. 490) noted that 'the present cathedral is being built of Horseforth [*sic*] Stone, a local Yorkshire grit stone'. The Horsforth area of Leeds had many quarries at this time, mostly working the Rough Rock (Millstone Grit), producing high quality building stone. The tracery, dressings, doorway and window surrounds and string courses, on the other hand, are of Ketton Stone (*Builder* 1901, p. 240) from the Middle Jurassic outcrops west of Stamford, Lincolnshire. This is a beautiful buff-coloured oolitic limestone, generally regarded as one of the finest examples of this kind of Jurassic stone, and is almost completely composed of small spheres of concentrically-deposited calcium carbonate (ooliths). Although the mixed use of limestone with sandstone is not normally recommended (see Chapter 6), no evidence of damage is yet apparent, so presumably the Rough Rock from Horsforth is a good quality stone. The interior uses a Bath Stone, another Middle Jurassic oolitic limestone reported (*Builder* 1901, p. 240) to be from Corsham Down near Bath, and the roof is of Delabole Slates from Cornwall. The 1838 St Anne's, designed by John Childs, was built of Stanningley Rock, a Coal Measures sandstone from Victoria Quarry, Stanningley, 5 miles west of Leeds (Barry 1839) — the only record found of the use of this stone in Leeds.

A short detour up Great George Street passes CATHEDRAL HOUSE (12:II*), the residence of the St Anne's clergy, which uses sand-faced Suffolk bricks with dressings and entrance surrounds of Ketton Stone. Beyond this is CATHEDRAL CHAMBERS (13:II), a 1990–91 redevelopment of the former Masonic Hall which was designed by J. M. Bottomley and built in 1900. The original building which fronts onto Great George Street is faced with red brick and red Corncockle Stone, a 'New Red Sandstone', for the dressings and string courses (*Building News* 1900, p. 73). This stone, which comes from Lochmaben near Lockerbie (Dumfries and Galloway) is basal Permian in age. The new building behind the old hall also has dressings of red basal Permian sandstones, but from Corsehill near Annan, also in Dumfries and Galloway, which proves to be a very good match for the original stone. The foundation stone for the Masonic Hall is a block of Shap granite.

Returning to Cookridge Street, the walk passes St Anne's to The Headrow. PERMANENT HOUSE (14, Plate 2a), built for the Leeds Permanent Building Society, is on the left and is included here as part of the Civic Buildings walk because of its importance as the first building to be completed for the major scheme to widen The Headrow. In 1924 the Leeds City Council decided that this main east-west route was too narrow for the traffic at that time. Plans were drawn up to demolish the whole of its north side from Cookridge Street to Eastgate and to redevelop it to a unified design. The architects for the scheme, Sir Reginald Blomfield and G. W. Atkinson, made an interesting choice to use Portland Stone and brick for the whole scheme. The Portland Stone quarries were certainly near the peak of their production in the mid-1920s, so the stone would have been relatively cheap and readily available in large quantities. It was transported to Leeds by rail. The selection of Portland Stone for the whole scheme probably reflected a desire on the part of the City Fathers to present a cleaner face to the new buildings and to reduce the soot blackening which badly affected all buildings using local sandstones. The decision to use this stone for the redevelopment of The Headrow led to its use for most major Leeds buildings through the late 1920s and the 1930s. It changed the look of the face of Leeds.

Permanent House was built in two stages. The part nearer The Headrow was opened in 1930; the remainder dates from the mid-1950s. Fine examples of the shelly variety of Portland Stone can be seen on some of the window sills of the Cookridge Street frontage, again showing the degree of weathering that has taken place since the building was finished. The Headrow street doorway is flanked by a pale grey-beige coloured granite. Pale Larvikite (Blue Pearl) panels frame the entrance, and on the sides of the windows the slabs are cut to have alternate polished and unpolished vertical stripes.

The WAR MEMORIAL(15:II) was originally (1922) sited in City Square, but was moved to its present position in The Headrow Garden of Rest in 1937. It is made of white marble from Carrara, Italy and shows very marked saccaroidal weathering. It has also been badly stained by waters running down from the bronze figures. The green slabs inset into the paving around the memorial are Lake District slates from Elterwater in the Great Langdale valley (Versey 1940, p. 300). A new bronze angel was fixed to the memorial in 1991.

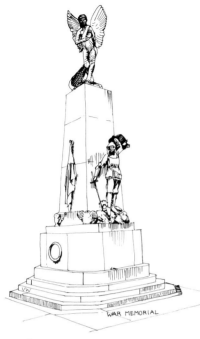

WAR MEMORIAL

The ART GALLERY (16:11, Figure 5), designed by W. H. Thorp, dates from 1887–88. The Centenary Street elevation was built of Bolton Woods Stone, Gaisby Rock (Coal Measures sandstone), from Bradford. The staircase balustrades, columns and vases in the entrance hall are fine examples of Hopton Wood Stone (Carboniferous Limestone); (*Building News* 1889, p. 99). The building was extended across Centenary Street in 1980–82 to form the HENRY MOORE SCULPTURE GALLERY. The new part of the Art Gallery is of clean-sawn blocks of Crosland Hill Stone from Huddersfield. This sandstone is an atypical example of the Rough Rock (Millstone Grit), because it is finer grained at Crosland Hill than is usual; typical Rough Rock is coarse grained. Henry Moore attended the Leeds Art School in 1919, and an example of his work 'Reclining Woman No. 80' (1980–82 in bronze) reclines uncomfortably in front of the building.

FIGURE 5.   The Art Gallery, with the Henry Moore Sculpture Gallery extension on the frontage, and the Henry Moore Institute on the right

This famous sculptor is remembered also by the opening in 1993 of the HENRY MOORE INSTITUTE (17, Figure 5), a conversion by Jeremy Dixon and Edward Jones of three nineteenth-century wool merchants' offices on the corner of Cookridge Street. The Headrow wall of this building is dramatically faced with an almost black igneous rock called Verde Prairi, a granodiorite from Quebec in Canada which is in fact very dark green in colour. The choice of this dark stone results in a feature which does not appear to be in sympathy, or for that matter connected, with its surroundings. The paving in front of the steps is made of cut slabs of Pule Hill Grit, 'Middle Grit Group' (Millstone Grit), from Clock Face Quarry, Rishworth, south-west of Halifax, and the stonework of the building (copings, gutters and sills) has been repaired with Rough Rock Flags (Millstone Grit), from Apperley Lane Quarry, between Apperley Bridge and Rawdon.

WALK 2: Commercial Buildings (1) — Park Row (Map 4)

Such a rich variety of materials has been used for the commercial buildings of Leeds that two walks are set out to cover the best of them.

Park Row has perhaps the finest range of both stones and building styles. The first walk is devoted to the two sides of this street, with a minor detour along Greek Street. The offices in Park Row are an important part of the heart of the City's economic life; the buildings reflect the pride and prosperity of each company as the banks and insurance firms competed with each other.

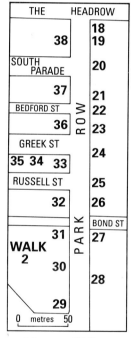

MAP 4.   Walk 2:
Commercial Buildings (1)
— Park Row

SAINT ANDREWS CHAMBERS

The walk starts at The Headrow end. There is nothing of particular note about the first building on the east side — ST ANDREW HOUSE (18:II), which is a good example of the use of brick with sandstone dressings. However, the next door SAINT ANDREWS CHAMBERS (19:II), built by George Corson for the Scottish Widows' Fund in 1869, is a good example of the typical Victorian use of Yorkshire sandstones. The upper walls are of fine-grained sandstone (hence from the Coal Measures), with much detailed and intricate carving particularly of thistles and other Scottish reminders of its original owners, resting on a base of coarse-grained sandstone (hence from the Millstone Grit). The second date, 1815, on the left hand side of the building is nothing to do with the age of the building, but notes the date the Company was founded. The roof of the entrance porch is supported by four Peterhead granite pillars, the left-hand one of which contains a fine dark-coloured xenolith. These granite pillars are remarkable examples of monoliths (that is, stones turned in one piece) which were made in great numbers by the Peterhead quarries at that time. They rest on collars of typical blue-grey Rubislaw granite from Aberdeen, which in turn rest on blocks of an unidentified coarse-grained, grey-white granite, possibly Ballybrew from Ireland.

PARK ROW HOUSE (20:II, Plate 2b) has recently been rebuilt (1989–90), retaining the original frontage of Alfred Waterhouse's splendid Prudential Assurance Building of 1894. The ground floor window surrounds are of Peterhead granite (Versey 1940, p. 297) which has lost its original polish and red colour, almost certainly when the building was badly cleaned. The original colour is shown by replacement blocks of new Peterhead granite which have been inserted below the middle window to the left of the entrance and by parts of the doorway surrounds. The upper floors are of red brick and Burmantofts butterscotch-coloured Faience. As part of the rebuilding, the original features of the top floor were restored using terracotta supplied by Shaws of Darwen.

ABTECH HOUSE (21:II, Plate 3a), built for the West Riding Union Bank in 1900 by the architects Oliver and Dodgshun, has a ground floor made of blocks of dark Larvikite (the variety Emerald Pearl) and a deep rich-red Swedish granite, probably the variety quarried from Venevik, with a purplish opalescent colour to the quartz crystals — a feature that is typical of some granites from

Sweden. The rest of the front elevation is made of Huddersfield Stone (*Building News* 1902, p. 541), the atypically finer-grained Rough Rock (Millstone Grit), from Crosland Hill Quarries. Above the ground floor, there is a splendid frieze, best seen from the other side of the street, stretching the full width of the building. Carved in sandstone, it depicts scenes highlighting the importance of banking in a wide range of commercial activities, and is one of the finest stone carvings on the buildings of Leeds. The crispness of the figures and the sharpness of the arrises is a quite remarkable testament to the quality of this sandstone. The sculptor's name 'THEWLIS SS' is carved on the stone; 'SS' means 'Sculpsit' that is 'sculpted this'. The roof is covered with Lake District Westmorland green slates.

Walking south down Park Row, the rest of the buildings beyond No.17 are all modern commercial sites, some of which show more imagination than others. The 1960s SCOTTISH MUTUAL HOUSE (22) was demolished in late 1995. It was a concrete building using crushed granite aggregate for the facing slabs. Otta Slate (also known as Rembrant Stone) was used for the flooring to the entrance and in front of the windows. This 'slate' is actually a mica-schist from Norway with small spherical red garnets and rods (up to 5 cm long) of hornblende (Pool 1972, p. 20). The replacement building was designed by Carey Jones. It has a structural-glazed front wall and the cladding to the stair core and flank walls is Karin Grey granite from Finland.

The next building, No. 14 PARK ROW (23, Plate 3b), formerly the Commercial Union offices, has an orange-coloured frontage, made of a Middle Jurassic cross-bedded, shelly oolitic limestone. This distinctive stone is from Guiting near Gloucester; a uniquely used and most unusual material for Leeds. With the whole building above the ground floor clad in this strongly-coloured oolitic limestone, the effect is to make the building stand out; it certainly is not in keeping with its surroundings and one would not expect to find this limestone in a sandstone City like Leeds. A variety of stones are used for the ground floor. The window surrounds are pale Larvikite and the facings around the door are rough, or rock-finished, pale-grey megacrystic south-west England granite. The architect, Mr H. Fairweather, wanted to face this building with Doulting Stone, which was used for Wells Cathedral, but supplies of that famous Jurassic limestone from Somerset were not available, so he used Guiting Stone instead.

ABBEY HOUSE (24, Plate 3b) has glistening panels to the upper floor which are of green schist from Northern Italy. The ground floor window facings are made of polished pale-grey south-west England granite, possibly from Merrivale Quarry, Dartmoor. The size of the white feldspar crystals can be compared with the larger crystals of the slightly different granite used on the building next door (23). The door facings, steps and window bases are of a black intermediate/basic, medium-grained igneous rock called Bon Accord from Sweden, which has small black metallic flecks (magnetite) that can be seen if the stone is looked at obliquely. These dark igneous rocks are difficult to identify without studying a thin section, but this example is an olivine-gabbro. Inside the doorway, the floor is of slabs of Lake District green slate, and the walls are of unstopped Roman Travertine. The surround of the building's index-board is of dark-grey 'marble' with white flecks. It is a limestone of Devonian age from Ashburton, Devon.

The building between Abbey House and the National Westminster Bank (25) uses Portland Stone in smooth-cut blocks for the upper floors and a fine-grained, grey-coloured possibly Scottish granite for the ground floor. The same granite is used in the NATIONAL WESTMINSTER BANK (26), on the Beckett's Bank site, with window uprights and door reveals made of another black intermediate/basic igneous rock, Swedish Ebony Black, which is a diorite.

South of Bond Street is the LLOYDS BANK building (27), designed by Abbey Hanson Rowe, and opened in 1977 on the site formerly occupied by Marshall and Snelgrove. The whole building from top to bottom, including the steps and surrounding pavements, is clad with the distinctive granite known as Baltic Brown (*The Architect* 1977, p. 45). This stone comes from Kotka in Finland, about half a mile from where the road to St Petersburg crosses the Russian border. It is easily recognized because of its colour and the prominence of spherical feldspar crystals with green reaction rims (known as rapakivi structures and named from the nearby town). The effect of using this dark stone is fine on a sunny day when the light reflects from the polished surface, but is heavy and gloomy on a dull day.

No. 1 PARK ROW (28), the last building on the east side of Park Row, was built in 1995–96 by Fletcher Joseph who specified cladding of Crosland Hill Stone, the atypically finer-grained Rough Rock (Millstone Grit) from Johnsons Wellfield Quarry at Huddersfield, with Balmoral Red granite from Finland for banding throughout. The name Balmoral dates from the time when Aberdeen was the granite-working centre of the world. Many granites were imported from Scandinavia and then sold on the British Market with British names such as Balmoral, Grey Royal and Imperial. Priestley House, the 1969 building on this site, was demolished in 1995. It had upper floors finished in exposed-aggregate panels, where the concrete is washed off the outer face of the blocks before it sets to give a rough stone surface, and dark Larvikite facing for the ground floor.

The northern part of the east side of Park Row therefore can be seen to have retained its Victorian character, but the southern part results entirely from post-1950 redevelopment. The west side, however, has a much more interesting mixture and retains more of its former grandeur.

Walking back up the west side of Park Row, the first site (29) was formerly occupied by the 1969 Norwich Union building which was demolished in 1995. The new building (1995–96), designed by Abbey Hanson Rowe, was planned to have cladding of reconstructed stone for the upper floors with Brazilian Aracruz 'Granite' for the lower part. The much-criticized Norwich Union building had lower floors faced with slightly grey-veined, white Carrara marble which weathered badly, and panels of pale Larvikite between the windows. The

MERCURY

general appearance, with panels larger than the windows and areas of grime in the vertical gaps between panels, was unattractive.

The foundation stone for the SUN ALLIANCE (30, Figure 6) is made of the same granite as the basal course and bears the date 28 April 1938. It was laid by the Postmaster General of the time. The building, typical for commercial buildings of the 1930s, uses smooth-cut blocks of white Portland Stone over a plinth course of polished, pale-grey granite of unknown origin (possibly Rubislaw). The door facings use polished slabs, probably of the same granite. The building, originally a Post Office administrative centre, has 'GRVI 1939' carved above the door. The carved head of Mercury, the messenger of the gods, with his winged helmet, looks down onto Park Row. This is best seen from the other side of the road. The Portland Stone below the building's name has weathered badly.

The WOOLWICH BUILDING SOCIETY (31:II, Figure 6) was built in 1892 for the York City and County Bank. It is another good example of the Victorian use of fine-grained Coal Measures sandstone, resting on a plinth of coarse-grained Millstone Grit sandstone blocks with vermiculated ornament. The superstructure was recorded as being carried out in Bradford Stone (*Builder* 1892, p. 66), probably the Gaisby Rock (Coal Measures), from Bolton Woods,

D

FIGURE 6.   Sun Alliance on the left, and the Woolwich
Building Society on the right

and the fine grain of this sandstone has allowed extensive carving, well seen in
the corner entrance which also has monolithic columns of Peterhead granite.

Across Bond Court, on the site of the former City Museum and Philosophical
Hall, is the MIDLAND BANK (32), opened in 1969. It is finished with concrete
slabs which used an aggregate made of crushed pale-grey granite (note
fragments of quartz, feldspar and flakes of white mica). For a concrete-faced
building, the result is not altogether unpleasant. The window bases are faced
with a medium-grained black intermediate/basic igneous rock. The sills inside

the windows are of Sicilian Pearl (Perlato di Sicilia), a Cretaceous limestone from Sicily with pronounced orange-coloured stylolites.

The next building is the four-square block of GREEK STREET CHAMBERS (33:II), built by Alfred Waterhouse in 1898 as Williams, Brown and Company's Bank. The ground floor is a favourite Victorian combination of pink Peterhead granite with grey granite from Dalbeattie, south-west of Dumfries, in the Criffell igneous mass (*Building News* 1896, p. 857). Small xenoliths add interest to the appearance of the latter stone. Peterhead columns are used in the doorway. The upper floors are of red brick ornamented with Burmantofts butterscotch-coloured Faience. The curb stones in front of this building are fine examples of Shap granite.

A short detour can be made along Greek Street to visit two interesting sites. AQUIS HOUSE (34) has a large planter on the step, clad with coarse-textured reddish-brown granite containing purplish opalescent quartz crystals. This is Imperial (or Dakota) Mahogany from Milbank, South Dakota, USA. The left-hand doorway reveal is of Swedish Bon Accord, an olivine-gabbro, but the right-hand one is made of slabs of cross-cut Swedish Green Marble, recording 16 April 1964 as the date when it was laid. Swedish Green is the trade name for this handsome stone, which is an ophicalcite (a serpentinous marble), formed by the metamorphism of a dolomitic limestone (see also Chapter 5:4:2).

The frontage of the next-door building, THE PODIUM (35), has been redeveloped (1990) using much brick, glass and plastic sheeting — an unattractive cheap-looking artificial modern material increasingly used for

BARCLAYS BANK

facings. However, the brick pillars on the Greek Street side are topped with blocks of red sandstone of Triassic ('New Red Sandstone') age which came from Birkhams Quarry at Sandwith, St Bees, near Whitehaven, Cumbria. This stone is also used on the Russell Street frontage (Pennine House) where it forms the entrance stairway and its treads. Some 'New Red Sandstones' are not particularly weather resistant, and it will be interesting to see how the stairway stands up to wear.

Returning to Park Row, the last three buildings at the north end show great contrast. The first, BARCLAYS BANK (36, Plate 4a), was built in 1922 to 1923. It is a dirty-white building and uses smooth-faced blocks, rusticated on the ground floor, of Portland Stone with some carving, on a plinth of rock-finished, pale-grey granite. The quoins on each side of the entrances are chamfered and extend to the top of the building. They are carved with a distinctive vermiculated ornamentation, reminiscent of that used for the bases of the lamp standards in front of the Town Hall (Walk 1:1).

The next building is also white, but is of totally different material. The ROYAL BANK OF SCOTLAND (37, Plates 2b & 4a) was built in 1909 by Perkin and Bulmer for the Scottish Union and National Insurance Company. It is a fine example of the white Marmo blocks and moulded ornamental faience manufactured from 1900 onwards by the Burmantofts tile works in east Leeds (*Building News* 1908, p. 905). It was cleaned successfully in 1992, retaining the original glaze. This material is similar to the Carrara Ware produced by Doultons of London, with which it can easily be confused. The building is noted (*Modern Building Record* Vol. 3, 1912, p. 52) as having a reinforced concrete frame, and is one of the earliest records of this fundamentally different style of construction in Leeds.

The last building on the west side of Park Row is another Victorian office block predominantly using Yorkshire sandstones. Now called SOVEREIGN HOUSE (38:11, Plates 2b & 4a), it dates from 1862 to 1864 and is the offices of Booth & Co. Solicitors. Designed by P. C. Hardwick for the Bank of England, it at one time housed the Bank of Credit and Commerce International. The fine-grained sandstone for the main walling is from Ringby, north of Halifax (*Building News* 1864, p. 569), the quarries being on the top of Pule Hill. This is one of the classic localities for Yorkshire sandstone, with a long history of quarrying. Good quality fine-grained Coal Measures sandstones are worked from a massive-bedded horizon within the Elland Flags. The building, when first constructed, was considered to be a 'new architectural ornament to the town'. Again, the base of the building is a massive coarse-grained Millstone Grit sandstone. The South Parade doorway has a fine surround and reveals made of Peterhead granite, one of the earliest uses of Scottish granite in Leeds. It is worth noting that Ringby Sandstone was used in 1779 for the Piece Hall in Halifax, probably the finest manufacturing hall in Yorkshire and one of the outstanding buildings in the county.

WALK 3: Commercial Buildings (2) — City Square to The Headrow via King Street and East Parade (Map 5)

MILL HILL CHAPEL (39:II, Plate 4b) is a convenient starting point for the second of the walks which describe the commercial buildings of Leeds. The Chapel has an interesting link with the early industrial history of Leeds: Joseph Priestley, who discovered oxygen, was the minister of the original seventeenth-century chapel from 1767–73. The congregation, formerly Presbyterian, is now Unitarian. The present chapel dates from 1848. It was designed by Bowman and

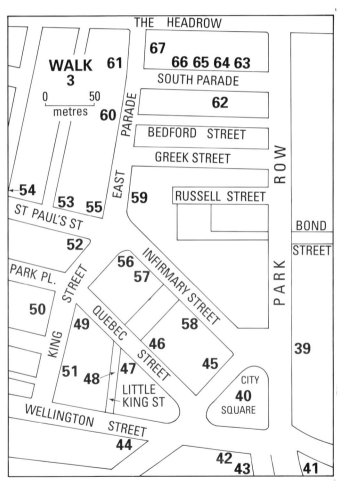

MAP 5. Walk 3: Commercial Buildings (2) — City Square to The Headrow via King Street and East Parade

Crowther and built of Rough Rock (Millstone Grit), a coarse-grained sandstone with quartz pebbles from Meanwood Quarries (Hopwood and Casperson 1986, p. 19). The relatively small blocks of stone used (compare them with the large blocks of the Civic Theatre; Walk 1:7) clearly show evidence of having been hand worked and chiselled. The sandstone blocks are decorated with zigzag or herringbone tool marks, a feature characteristic of nineteenth-century Meanwood Stone (Mr W. A. Hopwood, personal communication, 1994). This building must be one of the last in central Leeds to be made of hand-worked stone. In this respect it stands as a splendid monument to the skills of centuries of stone masons. Much of the carving is simple and bold, this being the style with coarse-grained Rough Rock stones. However, the more detailed carvings, for example the stops on the entrance gateway arch, are made of fine-grained Coal Measures sandstone. The appearance of this building has been dramatically changed by the removal of the pinnacles from the tops of the buttresses and turrets. Since these pinnacles are essential engineering features, it would be interesting to know why and when they were removed. The War Memorial in front of the chapel is of Portland Stone. The only distraction from this elegant and historic building is the appalling grey-painted south entrance porch, which is completely out of keeping with the splendid stone work of the rest of the building — a carbuncle if ever there was one!

CITY SQUARE (40), designed by William Bakewell, was laid out in 1902–03 with a display of statues and sculptures on the central island, which has since been modified several times to accommodate changing traffic needs. Plans were made in the 1890s when the Corporation decided to create a central square to try to enhance the cultural reputation of Leeds, and to celebrate its designation as a city in 1893. All the statues are Grade II 'listed' structures.

Sir Thomas Brook's (1903) equestrian figure is of the Black Prince who is said

THE BLACK PRINCE

in the course of his travels, and with the support of his father King Edward III, to have encouraged Flemish weavers to move to the West Riding, so giving a boost to the growing importance of the area as a wool marketing centre (*Builder* 1903, p. 368). This statue sits on a base and plinth of blue-grey Rubislaw granite from Aberdeen, some of which is polished and some has a rock-faced finish. The statue of the Black Prince, so story has it, arrived in Leeds on a canal barge!

The eminent Leeds men honoured in City Square are Joseph Priestley (1733–1804); Dean Hook, vicar of Leeds from 1837 to 1859; John

Harrison (1576–1656), builder of St John's Church and the Grammar School; and James Watt (1736–1819), whose steam engines powered the first factories in Leeds. The maidens are the famous figures of 'Morn' and 'Even' by Alfred Drury. The City Square statues were presented by T. W. Harding, a manufacturer of steel pins used in the combing process of the textile industries. All of these statues have bases of blue-grey Aberdeen granite and red Ross of Mull granite (H. C. Versey, Leeds Geological Association 1974 walk; notes supplied by W. J. Varker).

The OBSERVATORY (41:II, Figure 7), in the angle of Boar Lane and Bishopgate, was built in 1899 for the Yorkshire Banking Company by W. W. Gwyther. The main walling and the column capitals are of buff-coloured, fine-grained sandstone from the Gaisby Rock (Coal Measures), of Bolton Woods, Bradford. The carving is another example of the work of Joseph Thewlis of Leeds. The ten massive fluted attached columns (each of which consists of three drums) and the door surrounds are of red Ross of Mull granite, which originally was highly polished. The present washed-out colour is the result of the building being disastrously cleaned with dilute acid without protecting the surface of the granite, a treatment that has completely ruined the architectural integrity of this once handsome building. The moulded column bases and the upper part of the massive surbase of the building are of once-polished blue-grey Rubislaw

FIGURE 7.   The Observatory

granite from Aberdeen, resting on rough-finished rusticated blocks of the same granite (*Builder* 1899, pp. 491–92).

The whole of the south side of the square is taken up by the QUEEN'S HOTEL (42:II) and the railway office buildings, both of which are of Portland Stone. The hotel, completed in 1937, was designed by W. Curtis Green to be the grand frontage for the major CITY STATION (43) reconstruction which was being carried out at the time by the London, Midland and Scottish Railway (the initials LMSR can be seen carved high up on the east end of the Queen's Hotel). The late 1930s City Station had some fine features; the splendid concourse, for example, had a range of interesting stone facings. Most unfortunately, much of this former grandeur disappeared during the 1960s rebuilding, but remnants of the olive, gold and black-coloured quartzite tiles from Tuscany in Italy, used on the floor of the concourse (Versey 1940, p. 300), can be seen in the covered car park area, although they are now in very poor condition. The railway offices at the western end of the frontage has a base course of rough-finished pale-grey coloured south-west England granite. The Queen's Hotel, however, does not have a special base course.

Crossing Aire Street, the first building on the south side of Wellington Street is the GUARDIAN ROYAL EXCHANGE ASSURANCE offices (44). Crosland Hill sandstone (the atypical finer-grained Rough Rock (Millstone Grit), from Huddersfield) is used for the wall cladding. It rests on a base course of South American granitic gneiss known in the stone trade as 'Campo Grande Brazilian Granite' or 'Golden Carioca'. The sandstone is cut into standard-sized blocks and is laid in what is called range work. The lowest eleven courses have been treated, presumably to ease maintenance, and this has altered the colour of the stone.

The north-west side of City Square is taken up by H. Tanner's POST OFFICE (45:II, Figure 8) which was opened in 1896 to provide a background to the newly created Square. It is partly on the site of the 1758 Coloured Cloth Hall which closed in 1889. The walls of the Post Office are of medium-grained, buff-coloured Haworth Stone, a Millstone Grit sandstone (probably the Brandon Grit from the 'Middle Grit Group'), resting on a base course which is mainly coarse-grained pebbly sandstone. To the south of the doorway, blue-grey Rubislaw granite blocks from Aberdeen are used for the base course (*Building News* 1892, p. 335). Mr D. Gillson of Naylor Hill Quarry, Haworth has suggested (personal communication, 1993) that in the 1890s Barrett's West End Quarry on the south-west part of Penistone Hill, to the west of Haworth, would have been the most likely source for Haworth Stone. The building was cleaned in 1995.

The two entrances and the frontage between them have twelve columns which are monoliths of blue-grey Rubislaw granite. The columns rest on collars and blocks of medium-grained sandstone, and these on plinths also of Rubislaw granite. The door surrounds use the dark variety of Shap granite (Versey 1940, p. 297) which is seen to best advantage in the Infirmary Street entrance.

FIGURE 8.   The Post Office, with view along Infirmary Street to
Cloth Hall Court, the Yorkshire (Penny) Bank and No. 1 East Parade

OLD INFIRMARY GATE POST

Walking away from City Square along Quebec Street, the new (1990) entrance porch to NORWICH UNION HOUSE (46) is seen on the right. This is clad in blocks of fine-grained, buff-coloured Dunhouse sandstone, from near Staindrop, Co. Durham where beds low in the Millstone Grit are quarried. The base of this porch is suffering badly from rising salts.

On the opposite side of Quebec Street, QUEBEC HOUSE (47:II) is the Leeds and County Liberal Club of 1890, designed by Chorley and Connon. This fine late Victorian building is constructed of fiery-red brick and terracotta from Edwards of Ruabon in North Wales (*Builder* 1890, p. 396). The building was cleaned in 1994.

A short detour along Little King Street brings one to an old GATE POST (48) which survives from the 1771 Infirmary (Broadhead 1981,

p. 32). It is of rusticated blocks of fine-grained, buff-coloured sandstone which may have come from the Woodhouse Moor quarries where Elland Flags (Coal Measures) were worked. This gate post, now over 220 years old, is a remarkable relic and link with the building-stone history of Leeds.

On the King Street — Quebec Street corner is KINGS COURT (49, Plate 5a) completed in 1990. The walls are of buff-coloured Crosland Hill sandstone, from Johnsons Wellfield Quarry at Huddersfield where the atypical finer-grained Rough Rock (Millstone Grit), is quarried. The bases to the walls are clad in a fine-grained variety of Balmoral Red granite from Finland.

The new BANK OF ENGLAND (50, Figure 9) is on the west side of King Street opposite Kings Court. To obtain the best overall impression, the building should be viewed from the east side of the road before crossing to examine the detailed texture of the stone. The design of the building and the use of sheets of granite cladding throughout has resulted in an appropriately solid-looking structure, giving an impression of strength and stability. With bronze window frames it is virtually maintenance free. Myers (1972, pp. 11–14) gave an account of the selection of stone and the construction of the building which was opened in July 1971. Pelastine granite from a quarry at Mabe in the Cornish Carnmenellis mass, north of Falmouth, was chosen by the architect (H. W. Pearson) for the cladding of the whole building. A total of 310 cubic metres (1,000 tons) was taken by train to Aberdeen to be worked and then some 5,580 square metres of slabs, from two to four cms thick, were delivered to the site, again by train, and fixed between January 1970 and April 1971. The stone is a pale-grey coloured, coarse-grained biotite granite with prominent white feldspar crystals up to two cms long. Perhaps the most remarkable feature of this handsome granite is the marked flow banding of the darker ferro-magnesian minerals, with football-sized aggregations of the feldspar crystals. This texture shows that the magma was still molten after the first minerals — the white feldspars — had crystallized. It is well worth crossing the road to examine the details of this unusual granite texture. The only unfortunate feature of this impressive building is the unused and unconnected concrete walkway which sticks out at first floor level.

Before leaving the Bank of England site, look back across King Street from the corner of York Place to the fiery-red brick and terracotta METROPOLE HOTEL (51:II, Plate 5a) built in 1897–98, again by Chorley and Connon. This is another fine example of terracotta supplied by Edwards of Ruabon in North Wales (undated Edwards of Ruabon Catalogue, Mr Alan Garlick of Abbey House Museum Leeds, personal communication, 1994; see also Liberal Club, Walk 3:47). Incorporated into the roof of the hotel is the large stone cupola taken from the Fourth (1868) White Cloth Hall which was on this site.

Walking north up King Street, the white building on the corner of St Paul's Street is Perkin and Bulmer's ATLAS CHAMBERS (52, Figure 9). Dating from 1910, it is built of white Burmantofts Marmo Faience. Some of the tiles have

ATLAS

touches of green and pale-gold colour. Above the entrance, Atlas supports the world on his shoulders.

A short detour along St Paul's Street, the HEALTH and SAFETY EXECUT-IVE office (53, Plate 5b) is on the corner of Park Cross Street. This building is clad in richly-crinoidal Carboniferous Limestone, a variety known as Swale-dale Fossil Marble. It was worked from the Underset Limestone of Barton Quarry near Middleton Tyas, North Yorkshire. Weathering has badly affected the surface of this limestone which, in polished condition, is not a particularly good choice for exterior walling. All highly-polished calcareous stones such as limestone and marble used externally will loose their polish in the British climate. From this site there is a distant view of the colourful minarets of ST PAUL'S HOUSE (54:II, Plate 5b) which is between St Paul's Street and Park Square. Built in 1878 to the design of Thomas Ambler, it was originally a factory for Sir John Barran who pioneered the ready-made clothing industry. The terracotta was by Doultons of London (*Building News* 1879, p. 62). The building was redeveloped (1976) as offices, with the damaged sections of the minarets being repaired with fibreglass, and the terracotta being replaced by Shaws of Darwen.

No.1 EAST PARADE (55, Plate 5b), the offices of the Eagle Star Insurance Company, is one of the most recent additions to the Leeds scene, replacing the undistinguished 1960s Devereux House on the corner of St Paul's Street. The new building was designed by William Gower and Partners and built between 1992 and 1994; it is another modern example of the Multicoloured Leeds style. The main walling is faced in red brick with contrasting bands of blue and buff-coloured bricks. The dressings are of two different sandstones. For the early part of the construction, first to fifth floors, the dressings are of medium-grained sandstone from Buck Park Quarry, Cullingworth, south of Keighley, where ashlar blocks from the Rough Rock Flags (Millstone Grit), are worked. As construction progressed, thin dark streaks of fossil plant debris increasingly affected the quality of this stone, and the ground, sixth and seventh floors were completed with Brandon Grit (Millstone Grit), from Naylor Hill Quarry, Haworth, which is a coarser-grained sandstone. Both these sandstones were transported to Britannia Quarry, Morley to be cut and shaped. The ground floor base is clad with South African Bon Accord, a dark-grey to black basic igneous rock (gabbro). The roof is mainly of North Wales purple slates from Penrhyn, Bangor with contrasting bands of 'Camborne Light Grey' slates which were imported from Brazil. The entrance hall is marble lined, with Botticino

Classico from Italy for the walls and Breche Nouvelle from France for the skirting.

On the opposite side of the road, the ALLIED IRISH BANKS (56:II, Figure 9), on the corner of King Street and Infirmary Street, occupies Goodbard House which was built in 1905 on part of the site of the 1771 Infirmary. The upper walls are of a fine-grained, buff-coloured sandstone and the ground floor uses granites. The doorway surrounds and the columns are original, using slightly washed-out looking Peterhead granite, but the window surrounds are infills, at the time of recent rebuilding, and are of coarse-grained Balmoral Red granite from Finland. Although the source of the sandstone is not known, Goodbard House is an important site in the history of Leeds stone buildings. The sandstone is presumably from Yorkshire, and if so was the last major use of Yorkshire sandstone in central Leeds for many years. The next use of local stone was for the cladding of the Bond Street Centre (Walk 4:70) which was opened in 1977; 72 years after Goodbard House!

Passing down Infirmary Street towards City Square, the YORKSHIRE (PENNY) BANK (57:II, Plate 6a) also occupies part of the old Infirmary site. Designed by G. B. Bulmer, the building opened in 1894. It has a grey-granite basal course for the eastern end and for the entrances (source not discovered), with the walls above erected entirely of Morley Stone (*Builder* 1892, p. 486) which is from the Thornhill Rock (Middle Coal Measures). This fine Yorkshire

FIGURE 9.   The Allied Irish Bank, Goodbard House on the left, the Bank of England in the middle, and Atlas Chambers on the right

sandstone building had work on the foundations and basement carried out by one contractor, and work on the superstructure by another. One characteristic of the Thornhill Rock from Morley is that it changes colour when exposed to weathering. From grey or grey-buff when quarried, it changes in 18 months to 2 years time to a rich buff-brown colour because of the oxidization of iron minerals, but eventually changes again to paler buff. The contrast is well seen (1994) when comparing the 1894 Yorkshire Bank with the adjacent 1980 Cloth Hall Court, both of which use Morley Stone.

Further along Infirmary Street, CLOTH HALL COURT (58, Plate 6a) stands on the site of the Coloured Cloth Hall of 1758. It was designed by T. P. Bennett and Son, and opened in 1980. Fine-grained sandstone known as Woodkirk Stone, from the Thornhill Rock (Middle Coal Measures) of Britannia Quarry, Morley, near Leeds, is used to clad the building, and below the windows a red Swedish granite is used. The sandstone is a rich buff-brown colour.

Returning to East Parade, the ROYAL BANK OF SCOTLAND tower (59), Minerva House, is on the east side (No.29 and 30). The architects were D. J. Curtis and Associates and it was completed in 1990. Two types of stone are used for the exterior cladding, a pale grey-white granite from Sardinia, known as Sardinian Grey, and the distinctive Baltic Brown, a granite from Finland with marked green reaction rims to the large feldspar crystals (rapakivi structures; Walk 2:27). The third material used on the tower is another example of plastic sheets now being much used for cladding. The marble used inside the East Parade entrance is the dove-grey Carrara marble called Bardiglio Imperiale, an altered Jurassic limestone from Lucca in north-west Italy, a stone that was much used for Victorian fireplaces.

HEPPER HOUSE

Walking north along East Parade, two buildings on the west side of the road are of interest. EAST PARADE CHAMBERS (60:II) opposite Bedford Street was built in 1899. It is another good example of the use of Burmantofts decorative Faience with a recent extension using matching materials supplied by Shaws of Darwen. Further along the street No.17a, HEPPER HOUSE (61:II), now occupied by Phillips Auctioneers, is an early work of George Corson, dating from 1863. The buff-coloured sandstone of this building was recorded (*Builder* 1863, p. 424) as being from Harehills Quarry in north-east Leeds (Elland Flags, Coal Measures), with wall stones boasted, dressings rubbed, and bands of red sandstone in the arches and under the gables. The shafts to the windows are of polished red granite (Peterhead) for the porch and ground floor, and of 'serpentine' (probably from the Lizard, Cornwall) for the estate room and stairs. This is another historically valuable building, with one of the last usages of the classic pre-railway locally-quarried sandstones and the first recorded use of granite in Leeds.

Walking along South Parade, No. 15 at the Park Row end on the south side, is the EQUITY and LAW LIFE ASSURANCE SOCIETY offices (62). Much of the frontage is finished in a pale-grey granite, probably from Merrivale, Devon. The window piers are a variety of Larvikite. Below the windows, a black intermediate/basic igneous rock is used. The entrance has several interesting stones. The doorway sides through into the hall are a grey-green veined, white Carrara marble from north-west Italy, similar to the variety called Piastraccia. The hall flooring has tiles of a grey-veined white Carrara marble, probably the variety known in Britain (although not elsewhere) as Sicilian, and of a black limestone, probably Belgian, which has an irregular white patterning of calcite veins.

The north side of South Parade is notable for three buildings with extensive use of 'black granites' (dark-coloured igneous rocks) and illustrates the difficulties with the identification of these stones. No. 3 — PHOENIX HOUSE (63) has upper floors of Larvikite panels and Portland Stone ribs, whereas the ground floor uses a pale-grey granite (probably from south-west England), and a coarse-grained black intermediate/basic igneous rock. The black stone closely matches Swedish Bon Accord (olivine-gabbro).

No.4 — FOUNTAIN HOUSE (64) has smooth-faced blocks of Portland Stone for the upper floors, and for the ground floor another black intermediate/basic igneous rock which is medium grained (finer than that used for Phoenix House), and can be identified as Ebony Black (see comment regarding No.6–7 South Parade).

No.5 — the ICL building (65) is unremarkable except for the use of a fossiliferous limestone of Devonian age, probably from Belgium, for the facing of the canopy over the entrance (H. C. Versey, L. G. A. 1974 walk; W. J. Varker notes). It has weathered very badly in this position. However, corals and stromatolitic algal colonies can still be seen.

Nos. 6–7 SOUTH PARADE (66, Plate 6b) form the Legal and General building which was built in 1930–31. The style of this eye-catching black and white block is similar to that of No.4. The cladding for this building uses smooth-cut blocks of Portland Stone for the upper floors, and a medium-grained black igneous rock for the ground floor. H. C. Versey (L. G. A. 1974 walk; W. J. Varker notes) recorded this black stone as Ebony Black, a diorite from Sweden, and comparison with the black igneous rock used in No.4 (Fountain House) confirms that they are the same stone. The infill panels below the windows are made of cast iron! Returning to the South Parade-East Parade corner, the final building for this walk is William Bakewell's PEARL CHAMBERS (67:II, Plate 6b). This is another important site in the history of stone in Leeds, because it was one of the earliest major buildings in the city to use Portland Stone. It was built in 1911 for the Pearl Assurance Company and a statue of the company's founder stands high above The Headrow entrance. The upper floors use Portland Stone (*Building News* 1909, p. 905) in its three-dimensional style, extensively carved into a series of ornate pinnacles and figures. The whole of the ground floor is built of pale blue-grey Rubislaw granite from Aberdeen, and the stone work is load bearing. An interesting feature of Pearl Chambers, as with many of the late Victorian and early twentieth-century offices, is the carving of the building's name into the stonework, giving a feeling of great pride to its occupants and of permanency to the structure. The building was successfully cleaned and repaired in 1993, and the slate roof rehung.

   Great changes in the use and ornamentation of stone took place during the depressed times that followed the First World War. The marked contrast in style that resulted is well seen in the above two Portland Stone buildings in South Parade. The highly carved and decorated Pearl Chambers (1911) is a good example of the older three-dimensional style, whereas Nos. 6–7 South Parade (1930–31) is clad in smooth-cut blocks, which have been used since the 1920s.

WALK 4: Shop Fronts Leeds (Map 6)

The main retail shops of Leeds are in the broad rectangle bounded by Park Row, The Headrow, Vicar Lane and Boar Lane. The Shop Fronts walk covers the best of the cladding materials used in this area, to illustrate this aspect of the building stone history of Leeds. Many of the sites use relatively small quantities of stone, but a rich variety of colours and textures enhance the frontages.

The walk starts at the corner of Bond Street and Albion Street. ADAMS (68) has some of the finest slabs of Lake District green slate seen in Leeds, here used for the panels below the windows and for the pillar in the entrance. They are

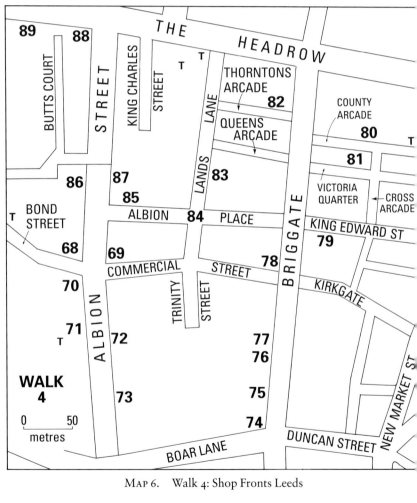

MAP 6.   Walk 4: Shop Fronts Leeds

Plate 1a.   Leeds Town Hall (Walk 1:1), with Oxford Place Methodist
Chapel (Walk 1:2) on the left

Plate 1b.   St Anne's Roman Catholic Cathedral (Walk 1:11)

Plate 2a.   Permanent House (Walk 1:14) and the corner of The Headrow, with St Anne's Cathedral (Walk 1:11) on the left

Plate 2b.   Park Row House (Walk 2:20), formerly the Prudential Building; with Sovereign House entrance (Walk 2:38) on the left, and the Royal Bank of Scotland (Walk 2:37), formerly the Scottish Union and National Insurance Company, on the right

Plate 3a. Abtech House (Walk 2:21), with carved frieze

Plate 3b. No. 14 Park Row (Walk 2:23), the former Commercial Union offices, on the left, and Abbey House (Walk 2:24) on the right

Plate 4a.   Barclays Bank (Walk 2:36) on the left, the Royal Bank of Scotland (Walk 2:37), formerly the Scottish Union and National Insurance Company, in the middle, and Sovereign House (Walk 2:38) on the right

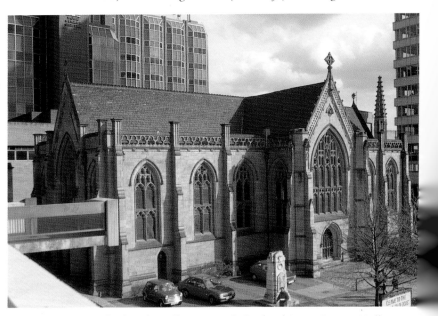

Plate 4b.   Mill Hill Chapel (Walk 3:39), with the Bond Street Centre (Walk 4:70) behind to the left

Plate 5a.   The Metropole Hotel (Walk 3:51), with Kings
Court (Walk 3:49) on the left

Plate 5b.   No. 1 East Parade (Walk 3:55), with the Health
and Safety Executive office (Walk 3:53) behind, and St Paul's
House (Walk 3:54) in the distance along St Paul's Street

Plate 6a. Cloth Hall Court (Walk 3:58) on the left, and the Yorkshire (Penny) Bank (Walk 3:57) on the right

Plate 6b. Pearl Chambers (Walk 3:67) on the left, and the Legal and General Building (Walk 3:66) on the right

Plate 7a.   The University Parkinson Building (Chapter 5.4.3)

Plate 7b.   Harewood House (Chapter 5.10) from the south, viewed across the
south-front terrace

Plate 8a.   The Corn Exchange (Chapter 5.16)

Plate 8b.   Leeds City (Kirkgate) Markets (Chapter 5.18)

typical of Borrowdale Volcanic ashes, showing evidence of original bedding, sedimentary structures and small-scale faults. They were quarried from Elterwater in the Great Langdale valley. The slabs were fitted in the early 1980s and still retain their fresh green colour. When exposed for long periods, however, Borrowdale Volcanic slates tend to lose their colour and take on a washed-out look.

Albion Street was created as recently as 1792 on vacant land, and was originally for superior residences, with no shops being allowed. It has now been extensively rebuilt for retail and commercial use, but something of the early nature of the street is preserved in the adjacent Albion Place and Commercial Street (see Chapter 1).

One of the oldest buildings in Albion Street to survive is MOORLANDS HOUSE, the Britannia Building Society office (69:II) which was built for the Leeds and Yorkshire Assurance Company by W. B. Gingell in 1852–55. It was one of the first of the large new commercial office blocks to be built in Leeds. *The Builder* (1858, p. 466) recorded that three of the classic local Leeds sandstones were used. The plinth is built of large, boldly vermiculated, rusticated blocks of Bramley Fall Stone, Rough Rock (Millstone Grit). The finely-rusticated ground floor and the Venetian windows used stone from Pool Bank Quarry, in the Caley Crags Grit (Millstone Grit), and the two upper storeys with columns used Rawden Hill Stone, from the Lower Follifoot Grit (Millstone Grit). It is interesting to note this reminder of Victorian grandeur amongst the retail shops of Leeds. The building is another remarkable monument to the early Victorian quarrymen and to the masons of Leeds.

MOORLANDS HOUSE

BOOTS (70) is situated on the opposite corner of the Bond Street–Albion Street junction and is part of the major Bond Street Centre redevelopment (Plate 4b) opened in 1977. Blocks of fine-grained, rich buff-brown coloured sandstone are used to face the walls. They are of Woodkirk Stone from Britannia Quarries, Morley, where the Thornhill Rock (Middle Coal Measures), is worked. Some blocks show small scale cross-bedding structures, picked out with flecks and layers of darker grains (probably an iron mineral). As already noted, the Bond Street Centre stone cladding was the first use in 72 years of Yorkshire sandstone in Leeds since Goodbard

House (Walk 3:56) was built. The Planning Board insisted on the use of this cladding for such a prestigious site.

Passing south down Albion Street, the BOND STREET CENTRE entrance (71) has an interesting stone paving. The bulk of its flooring is of stopped Roman Travertine, a redeposited calcium carbonate rock (limestone) of Tertiary age from one of the Tivoli Quarries, near Rome, Italy. Unfortunately the resin stoppings have come away from the stone, allowing the naturally occurring holes to enlarge and become very dirty. Some of the blocks outside the entrance have failed and have been replaced by an entirely different type of limestone known as Sicilian Pearl (Perlato di Sicilia), a Cretaceous limestone with marked orange-coloured stylolites. An ornamental edging to the entrance floor runs through the whole Centre. It is of Swedish Red Polar Marble, a fine-grained, reddish-brown muddy limestone of Ordovician age from Brunflö, Järntland, Sweden. This stone, sometimes known as Swedish Orthoceras Limestone, contains cross-sections of the well-preserved fossil cephalopod *Orthoceras*, which has a straight chambered shell. The walling inside the Centre uses slabs of stopped Roman Travertine. The entrance hall of No.11 of the Bond Street Centre is faced with good examples of this latter material.

On the opposite side of Albion Street, PROVINCIAL HOUSE (72) has recently (1993) been redeveloped, using cladding of Sardinian Pink granite.

The CO-OP store (73), on the east side towards the bottom of Albion Street, uses heavily brecciated and white-veined green serpentinite for the window surrounds. Particularly good slabs form the reveals in the entrance doorway nearest to Boar Lane. A great range of serpentinites are available from Italy and Greece with subtly differing colours, textures and figuring. The Co-op variety is known as Vert St Denis Classico and comes from Val d'Aosta, north-west of Turin, Italy.

Turning east out of Albion Street, the walk continues along Boar Lane to McDonalds on the corner of Briggate, passing Holy Trinity Church and with views of the Corn Exchange at the end of Duncan Street (see Chapter 5.15 and 5.16 for details of these two buildings). A major redevelopment of the south side of Boar Lane started in 1990.

The McDONALDS (74) chain so commonly uses well-polished stopped travertine for their shop fronts that the stone is sometimes referred to as 'McDonald's Stone'. The Briggate shop is a typical example. Note that the bedding of the stone runs up and down the slabs and is well matched from slab to slab. The stone, known as St Johns or Silver Moonlight Travertine, comes from a quarry at Serre di Rapolano near Siena, central Italy. The inset panels of dark, medium-grained igneous rock (gabbro) is a variety of Bon Accord called Nero Tijuca from South Africa.

Walking north up the west side of Briggate the next stop is at BURGER KING (75) which is faced with 30 cm square slabs of a high-grade metamorphic rock, a gneissic granite known as Juparana from Brazil.

The next building of interest along Briggate is the 1950s MARKS & SPENCER (76) on the site of the former Rialto cinema. The original building has upper floors faced with a black intermediate/basic igneous rock, and a similar stone is also found below the windows. The upper one is Swedish Ebony Black, a diorite; the lower one is dark grey South African Bon Accord, an olivine-gabbro. The ground floor facings around the windows are of a pale-grey granite from Hantergantick Quarry, Bodmin Moor near St Breward, north-east of Wadebridge, in Cornwall. Inside the store, the blocks of green stone at the head of the stairs leading down to the basement are of the same Swedish Green Marble (ophicalcite) that is used at Aquis House (Walk 2:34). An extension to Marks & Spencer was completed in 1994, on the left-hand side of the building. Below the windows, dark-grey South African Bon Accord is again used. The flow-banded, pale-grey granite surrounding the windows is Cornish De Lank Silver Grey. De Lank Quarry is less than a quarter of a mile south-west of Hantergantick Quarry. Both quarries are now owned by Natural Stone Products. Although they work the same Bodmin granite mass, the stone from each is subtly different in colour and character.

To the north of Marks & Spencer is THORNTON & CO. (77), built as the India Rubber Manufacturers premises. Designed by S. D. Kitson in about 1918, the upper floors are made of white Burmantofts Marmo Faience.

H. SAMUELS (78), on the north side of the Commercial Street junction, has facings around the windows and a pillar in the corner entrance consisting of an unusual example of Carboniferous Limestone. It is called Napoleon Marble and is quarried from the Boulonnais area of the Pas de Calais, not far from the north French coast (Dimes 1988, pp. 21–24). The name is derived from the fact that Napoleon's invasion fleet was assembled on the coast near the quarries, and the column which supports his statue near Boulogne is made of this stone. The layering in the limestone is probably due to stromatolitic algal growth. There are also pockets crowded with brachiopod shells, plus a few gastropods. The cavities of the fossils are filled with secondarily deposited calcite. Careful examination of the cross-sections of some of the brachiopod shells shows that a few examples are partly filled with sediment which had consolidated before the other part was later infilled with calcite. The line separating these two infills is a fossil spirit-level. These features are known geologically as geopetals, and preserve the angle at which the limestone was originally laid down. The polish of this limestone has deteriorated very badly because of exposure, and the best surfaces are inside the entrance where they are protected from the weather.

Across Briggate, the King Edward Street frontage of DEBENHAMS (79) is faced with Siena Yellow (or Giallo di Siena), a classic yellow-brown marble with black veins from the Siena area in Tuscany, central Italy (Versey 1940, p. 300). It is probably the variety called Brocatelle Siena. Unfortunately, this stone is in very poor condition. Some years ago it was varnished, an ill-advised attempt at maintenance. The varnish is now peeling from the surface leading to

FIGURE 10.   County Arcade, and the Victoria Quarter

its present distressing appearance. Perhaps one day the money will be found to re-polish this frontage and return the stone to its original handsome and attractive state.

On the east side of Briggate, Queen Victoria Street has recently been roofed over, and the COUNTY AND CROSS ARCADES (80:11, Figure 10) extensively refurbished (1989–90). The whole area is now known as the VICTORIA QUARTER (81:11). The County and Cross Arcades were built by Frank Matcham in 1898–1900 to provide high-class shops in this part of Leeds. Red brick and Burmantofts butterscotch-coloured Faience was used for the exterior walls above ground floor level, and above the shops in the arcades the whole is richly finished with a variety of brightly-coloured Faience.

The flooring of the former Queen Victoria Street has been laid with large slabs of pale-grey Hantergantick granite, and a black igneous rock with the name 'Frankland Grey'. The latter stone is the same as South African Bon Accord, an olivine-gabbro. Red Peterhead granite is used on the vertical faces of the raised flower beds and the fountain. The central block of the fountain is carved in 'Light Roman Stone' which is an oolitic limestone from Portugal, not Italy as its name suggests, and shows some rather crudely-carved representations of fossils. The cafe table tops are of grey-veined Carrara marble.

Throughout the Victoria Quarter, the shop windows have surrounds of a mid-grey-coloured variety of Larvikite. The different colour of the replacement slabs shows the difficulties of matching this stone and illustrates the wide range of variation that occurs within this one igneous mass. At the Briggate end of County Arcade the Larvikite pilasters rest on bases of a red granite known as

Tranas Red from Sweden. Between the shops in County Arcade, the columns and pilasters are made of excellent examples of a strongly brecciated and colourful marble which is presumably Italian, although its source has not been discovered (Versey 1940, p. 300). These rest on bases of a pale-red marble which matches Rosso Verona, a Jurassic stone from Veneto in Italy. The twelfth base from the Briggate end on the north side of the arcade, and the pilaster to the left of the arch next to it, show the outlines of large coiled ammonites (H. C. Versey, L. G. A. 1974 walk; Ian Duncan notes). Some of these brecciated stones have been carefully repaired using painted plaster! The three floor mosaics are composed dominantly of marbles and were relaid in 1989.

The walk continues to Lands Lane through THORNTON'S ARCADE (82:11) built in 1875–78 by Charles Thornton, the then proprietor of the City Varieties. This was the first of the shopping arcades which were to become a characteristic feature of Leeds. It was constructed along the line of the Old Talbot Inn Yard, one of the long narrow burgage plots which ran at right angles to Briggate, and so helps to preserve the distinctive layout of medieval Leeds. Some of the original 1878 shop fronts of grey Rubislaw granite from Aberdeen, with their brass air-vents, still survive at the west end of the arcade. The clock was installed in 1878 and the figures are of Friar Tuck, Richard Cœur de Lion, Robin Hood and Gurth the Swineherd, all characters from Scott's Ivanhoe.

Turning south down Lands Lane, DOLCIS–MISS SELFRIDGE (83) is part of the redeveloped Scala Cinema site. The shop front facings are of Sicilian Pearl (Perlato di Sicilia), a pale, buff-coloured polished Cretaceous limestone with orange-coloured stylolites. The blocks are well laid so that the horizontally-running stylolites are matched from one slab to the next. The plinth course is made of Sardinian Pink granite, and an interesting effect is created by the use of alternating polished and rock- or hammer- finished unpolished stones. This pleasing and attractive development is partly spoiled by having grey-veined Carrara marble for the entrance flooring. Some of the slabs have cracked and deteriorated, an indication that they were badly laid. The upper floors are of brick and buff-coloured terracotta tiles.

The short walk down Lands Lane to Pack Horse Yard, on the east side between Albion Place and Commercial Street, brings one to a Leeds Civic Trust Plaque erected in 1994 to record an important item of Leeds history. The plaque commemorates Joseph Aspdin, a Leeds bricklayer who lived in this yard. In 1824 he patented Portland Cement, from that time on a vital building material.

The pedestrian areas of Bond Street, Commercial Street, Albion Street, Albion Place and Lands Lane were redeveloped in 1991–92, to provide a more attractive setting to this key shopping area. Designated as LANDMARK LEEDS (84), the scheme uses red tiles from Ruabon, North Wales, Blue Baggeridge bricks from Kimsbury near Tamworth, Staffordshire, and coarse-grained Balmoral Red granite with coloured fibreglass insets for the pavements. The same Balmoral granite is used to clad most of the street furniture. The terracotta signs at the entrances to the area were supplied by Shaws of Darwen.

From Lands Lane, Albion Place should be followed to Albion Street, passing on the left the old County Court (1870:II) and Austin Reed, the former YMCA building (1900), and on the right (No. 3) the Leeds Club (1850s:II). At the west end of the street, No. 1 ALBION PLACE (85:II, Figure 2) is an impressive Georgian townhouse built in 1794–95 using red brick, with fine-grained, buff-coloured sandstone for the string courses and plinth. The house, an interesting reminder that this was originally a fashionable residential area, was built for the surgeon William Hey; it is at present the home of the Leeds Law Society.

A little way along the west side of Albion Street, the TSB office (86) has two granites. The cladding to the frontage is a rich-red Swedish granite known as Carnation Red (or Vanga or Napoleon). The slabs to the right of the doorway show flow banding with the accumulation of feldspar crystals, and include xenoliths of country rock which have almost been assimilated into the granite. The reveal on the north side of the doorway is of grey-beige Sardinian granite with large feldspar crystals, known as Sardegna Grey. This was fitted in about 1985. The reveal on the south side was fitted in the 1960s and is not the same granite. The source of the latter has not been discovered.

On the opposite side of Albion Street from the TSB is BERRYS JEWELLER (87). It is faced with green serpentinite, but three different varieties have been used. The left-hand part of the shop is a 1993 extension with relatively bright green slabs of Verde Tinos from the Greek Isle of Tinos. The two markedly different serpentinites used for the original frontage are slightly faded, but they both come from the same quarry at Val d'Aosta, north-west of Turin, Italy. The slabs above and to the right of the central window are of a finely-brecciated stone with thin white veins, a variety known as Vert St Denis Cobweb. The right-hand part of the frontage uses strongly-brecciated stone with wide veins, a variety called Vert St Denis Classico. This interesting site demonstrates the great difficulties of identifying varieties of serpentinite without precise source information.

Holbeck House, the head office of the LEEDS AND HOLBECK BUILDING SOCIETY (88) on the corner of Albion Street and The Headrow, was opened in 1930 and has a 1970 extension. It was built of white Portland Stone and brick to conform with The Headrow redevelopment. A variety of green serpentinite known as Verde d'Alpe from St Pauls Quarry, Basses-Alpes in France is used in the Albion Street entrance. Door surrounds are of a pale-grey, pink-tinged granite which is probably Sardinian. The Burley Bar Stone (see Chapter 5.22) was sited here on The Headrow frontage, and this historical marker, which is a block of fine-grained Coal Measures sandstone, is now preserved in a glass case within the building society office.

Walking west along The Headrow, the final stop for this walk is THE GUILDFORD public house (89) on the corner of Green Dragon Yard. Ever since 1775–78 there has been an inn on this site (known as Butts or Merryboys Hill). The old name of Duncan Inn was later changed to the Green Dragon. The present building, its name changed to the Hotel Guildford in 1920–21, is a good late Victorian-Edwardian example of Multicoloured Leeds, using brick and fine-grained, buff-coloured sandstone. Threatened with demolition in 1984, the brewery was forced to undertake renovation and then won the 1988 Leeds Award for Architecture for the best altered building of the year. The table tops in this pub are of the best-quality white Carrara marble (Statuario or First Statuary White Marble).

The Shop Fronts walk ends here, close to The Headrow–Park Row corner, and so a stop-off in The Guildford to examine the table tops and sample the ales, not necessarily in that order, makes a satisfactory conclusion to a walk illustrating some of the best of the retail-shop cladding stones of central Leeds.

The help that Mr Keith Denton gave with details of the Shop Fronts cladding stones was an invaluable contribution to this walk.

CHAPTER 5

Further Afield: Well Worth A Visit

The four walks in Chapter 4 cover the best examples of building stones and the changing styles in central Leeds. There are, however, many other important buildings which are either in outlying areas or do not fit conveniently into the routes of the walks. Some of these are of historical interest and others use stones that are unusual or even unique to Leeds. They are here listed and described, starting with the sites in the Kirkstall area of the Aire valley, continuing in a generally clockwise direction round the north of Leeds (Maps 2 and 7), finishing with St Peter's Church, the Bar Stones, and Windsor House.

The Gradings of the 'LISTED BUILDINGS' are again noted, and are in brackets following the headings where appropriate.

5.1 *Kirkstall Viaduct* (II)

The Leeds and Thirsk Railway viaduct is one of the finest monuments in the Leeds area to the massive achievements of the railway engineers. Built in 1846 to the design of Thomas Grainger, it carries the line across the Aire valley on a graceful curve. The flat-arched bridge across the Leeds and Liverpool Canal is a particularly fine structure. The stone used is the coarse-grained pebbly sandstone from a quarry in the Bramley Fall area that worked the Rough Rock (Millstone Grit). The viaduct was cleaned in 1988–89.

5.2 *Kirkstall Abbey* (I)

Kirkstall Abbey, in the Aire valley about three miles north-west of Leeds, was founded in 1152 as a daughter house of Fountains Abbey. It is one of the finest early Cistercian abbeys in the country, taking only about twenty years to build. The fact that the buildings then stood little altered through to the dissolution in 1539 is a major tribute to the stone used in its construction. The stone is the coarse-grained, grey-weathering pebbly and cross-bedded sandstone from Bramley Fall and other quarries in this part of the Aire valley. These are the renowned localities where one of the most durable of sandstones, often referred to as Bramley Fall Stone, from the Rough Rock (Millstone Grit), was quarried. The relatively undecorated state of much of the Abbey's stonework may in part result from the difficulties of making fine carvings in this tough coarse-grained rock. A weir may have been built across the River Aire south of the Abbey site, to enable barge-like boats to be used to float the stone the short distance downstream from Bramley Fall. Kendall and Wroot (1924, p. 708) noted that the quarry at 'Kirkstall Forge is the lineal descendant of workings instituted in the Twelfth Century by the monks of the abbey'.

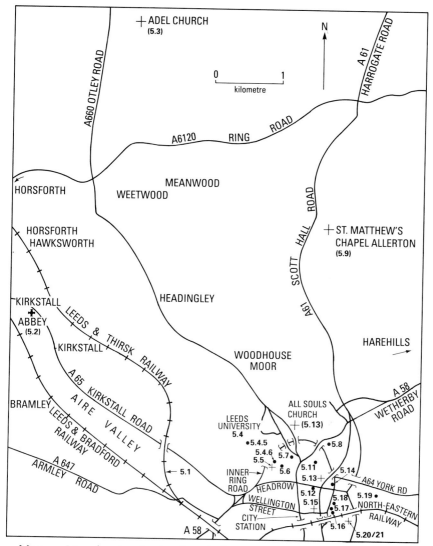

MAP 7.   Map showing the sites described in Chapter 5 — Further Afield: Well worth a visit

5.3 *Church of St John the Baptist, Adel* (A, Figure 1)

Adel Church must be one of the best examples of unaltered Norman architecture in Britain. It has two fine, extensively carved arches with chevron or zig-zag ornamentation. Much of the detail of the south-doorway carving has unfortunately deteriorated badly in the last 100 years (Sprittles 1969; compare plate 12 taken about 1871 with plate 13 taken in the 1960s). However, the detail of the chancel arch is still sharp. The building of the nave of this small, simple structure probably started between 1150 and 1155, but most of the church dates from 1160 to 1170. There may have been an earlier Saxon church on the site.

The bulk of the building, inside and out, is of a coarse-grained, buff-coloured, buff-grey weathering sandstone with no conspicuous quartz pebbles. Almost certainly it is not the Rough Rock (Millstone Grit); the carving of the two arches is in far finer detail than would have been possible with that particular sandstone. There are a few blocks of the distinctive Rough Rock, especially in the west wall, but possibly these are replacements. Rough Rock was used also for repairs to the tracery of the two large windows in the south wall which were added in the sixteenth century. The font is made of a block of coarse-grained sandstone without conspicuous quartz pebbles; as with the building, it is probably not Rough Rock.

Adel Church stands on a broad plateau of sandstone belonging to the Huddersfield White Rock (Millstone Grit), but faulting to the south brings in older horizons. Several small quarries are shown on the 1851 Ordnance Survey topographical map of the area. The closest is about 400m south-east of the church, on the east side of Long Causeway. This quarry lies south of a fault, and worked the Guiseley Grit (Millstone Grit). It is possible that this is the sandstone used in the construction of Adel Church.

5.4 *Leeds University*

The Yorkshire College, founded in 1874, became the nucleus of the new independent University when it was established in 1904. The University's building history is in three periods, each with its own clearly distinctive style and materials. During the first period, Alfred Waterhouse (1877–1904) and his son Paul (1905–12) were the architects. They built the College Road frontage, including the Textile Buildings, the Great Hall and the Baines Wing. Red brick with sandstone dressings were used for the whole of this development. The second period of construction is known as The Prize Scheme. It followed the Competition held in 1925–26 for the design of future buildings, which was won by Lancaster, Lucas and Lodge. This scheme was not completed until the early 1960s. Although some brick was used, all frontages were clad in white Portland Stone. The decision to use Portland Stone was taken by the university authorities in consultation with the architects. The comparatively small additional cost of this material was felt justified for the sake of the 'added dignity' gained from stone facing. The introduction of Portland Stone into a 'Midland Industrial centre' was noted, and doubts expressed about the durability of limestone in the Leeds atmosphere (*Quarry, Surveyors and Contractors Journal* 1928, p. 82). The third construction period saw the Chamberlin Plan, the first phase of which started in 1963. This belongs to the ferro-concrete age.

The first buildings of the Alfred Waterhouse plan to be finished were the Textile Buildings, which were funded by the Clothworkers' Company and opened in 1880. The materials used were red pressed brick, with stone dressings from the Spinkwell Quarries, near Bradford (*Building News* 1880, p. 207). These quarries were just south of the present Bolton Woods Quarry and have long been disused. They worked the celebrated Gaisby Rock (Coal Measures), and produced some of the classic Bradford sandstones, including 'Spinkwell Blue' and 'Spinkwell Brown'. Gosden and Taylor (1975, p. 151), in their history of Leeds University, quoted from a 1908 brochure produced to commemorate the opening of Leeds University, that all the Waterhouse buildings fronting onto College Road 'were faced externally with red pressed brick, and had dressings of Bolton Woods Stone', again the Gaisby Rock sandstone from the Coal Measures.

5.4.1 GREAT HALL (II, Figure 11)

The Great Hall, built of red brick with buff-coloured sandstone dressings of Bolton Woods Stone (Gaisby Rock, Coal Measures) and opened in 1894, was an addition to Alfred Waterhouse's original Yorkshire College plans. A striking feature is the colourful Burmantofts Faience on the staircase leading to the first

FIGURE 11.   The University Great Hall

floor hall. This is another of the many examples of Waterhouse's use of Burmantofts Faience. The vestibule floor-mosaic was originally a mixture of limestones and marbles (*Builder* 1894, p. 264), but was relaid in 1992 with centre, surrounds and panels of Rosso Verona, Bianco Carrara and black limestone.

5.4.2 BROTHERTON LIBRARY (II)

The Brotherton Library was opened in 1936 as a central and important part of the Lancaster, Lucas and Lodge scheme. The reading-room rotunda is splendidly decorated with two classic building stones.

The library entrance and the stairways up from the reading-room floor are clad with highly-polished Hopton Wood Stone (Carboniferous Limestone) from quarries near Matlock in Derbyshire. The pilasters and pillars are made of well-patterned Swedish Green Marble (Versey 1940, p. 298; *Architect & Building News* 1936, p. 37). This handsome marble, originally a dolomite, has prominent green-coloured banding. In geological terms it is an ophicalcite. The twenty massive columns are constructed of three drums, each of which weighs three tons. They have bronze capitals and bases. Swedish Green has been worked at Østergothland since 1650 or even earlier. The quarry was specially reopened to supply the stone for the Brotherton Library columns. One of the drums was found to be faulty when delivered, and had to be replaced. This is a remarkable example of the use of a classic building stone, perhaps the finest in Britain.

5.4.3 PARKINSON BUILDING (II, Plate 7a)

The Parkinson Building with its great hall and dominant tower, forming the central feature and main entrance for the Woodhouse Lane frontage of Lancaster, Lucas and Lodge's major expansion scheme, was designed by T. A. Lodge. Work began in the spring of 1938 but the building was not fully opened until 1951, after having been used as a Ministry of Food store during the Second World War. White Portland Stone was used for the exterior cladding which rests on a plinth course of rock-faced pale-grey south-west England granite. The hall interior is also faced with slabs of Portland Stone, used for both the walls and the fluted pillars, which it should be noted are not solid. The entrance flooring is of stopped travertine.

5.4.4 UNIVERSITY WAR MEMORIAL

The University is fortunate to have a fine example of work by the famous sculptor Eric Gill as its War Memorial. The sculpture of 'Our Lord driving the moneychangers out of the Temple' aroused considerable controversy when it was dedicated in 1923. It is carved in five blocks of Portland Stone, joined to make a single scene. Originally the Memorial was sited in the open on the south wall of the old library, adjacent to the Baines Wing entrance, where it was exposed to the weather. Portland Stone is a white oolitic limestone, the surface of which reacts with sulphuric acid in a polluted atmosphere to form the mineral gypsum. This process is known as sulphation (see Chapter 6) and results in the stone forming a dirty pale-buff coloured crust if not washed clean by rainwater. By 1939 the stone had darkened and Gill was asked about steam cleaning. No action was taken, and it was never cleaned. In 1961 the Memorial was moved to its present position in the New Arts Building and placed in the entrance foyer of the Rupert Beckett Lecture Theatre.

5.4.5 ADULT CONTINUING EDUCATION CENTRE, SPRINGFIELD MOUNT (II)

The Adult Continuing Education Centre in Springfield Mount was formerly the Hostel of the Resurrection, or the Priory of St Wilfrid. It was founded by the Community of the Resurrection to enable less-well-off students to enter the Anglican priesthood by reading for a degree at Leeds University.

The design, which is late fourteenth century in style, was by Temple Moore. Building was begun in 1908 but not completed until 1928. The east wing and the tower were the first parts to be built. The walls are of red sand-faced bricks from Boroughbridge, North Yorkshire, with strong quoins, window and door surrounds, and other dressings in a medium-grained, grey-weathering sandstone from Pool Bank Quarries where the Caley Crags Grit (Millstone Grit) was worked (*Modern Building Record* Vol. 4, 1913, p. 104).

5.4.6 LEEDS SCHOOL OF MEDICINE, THORESBY PLACE (II, Figure 12)

The Leeds School of Medicine (known as the Old Medical School), which currently houses the University's Departments of Microbiology and Chemical Pathology, is in Thoresby Place next to the General Infirmary. It was built in 1893–94 to the design of W. H. Thorp. The exterior walls are of high-quality red bricks with fine-grained, buff-coloured sandstone dressings from Morley Moor, where the Thornhill Rock (Coal Measures) has long been quarried (*Builder* 1893, p. 30). The main entrance has a porch, with a marble mosaic

FIGURE 12. The University School of Medicine

floor, leading to a hexagonal hall with arcaded sides lined with green
Burmantofts Faience. Above the arches, the walls are faced with smooth-dressed
blocks of Red Mansfield Stone (*Builder* 1894, p. 264), a pale-red coloured sandy
facies of the Lower Magnesian Limestone of Permian age, and quarried at
Mansfield, Nottingham. This famous building stone has been widely used
throughout Britain.

The Old Medical School is one of the best examples of the brick and
sandstone-dressing style of Multicoloured Leeds.

5.5 St George's Church, Great George Street (C, Figure 13)

St George's Church stands at the western end of Great George Street, on the
opposite side of Thoresby Place from the General Infirmary. It was built in
1836–38 of coarse-grained, grey-weathering, pebbly sandstone from Horsforth
(*Builder* 1901, p. 490), to the design of John Clark. The quarries in this area of
north-west Leeds worked the Rough Rock (Millstone Grit). The spire blew
down in the great gale of 11 February 1962 (Clarke 1989, p. 30) and has not
been rebuilt. The Long Room extension on the north side of the church was
built in 1974 using Woodkirk Stone (Thornhill Rock, Coal Measures) from
Britannia Quarry, Morley, Leeds. The present rich buff-brown colour of this
distinctive sandstone can be compared with the buff colour of the same stone
which was used for the adjacent 1894 School of Medicine at the top of Thoresby
Place. The door and windows at the eastern end of the extension were inserted
in 1990, and the surrounds are built of buff-coloured, medium-grained Rough
Rock Flags sandstone (Millstone Grit), from Hawksworth Quarry, Odda Hill,
Guiseley, Leeds (see Chapter 5.8).

5.6 General Infirmary, Great George Street (I, Figure 13)

The Gothic-styled General Infirmary is another fine example of a Multicoloured
Leeds building constructed of brick with sandstone dressings. George Gilbert
Scott (who also designed St Pancras Station in London), was the architect for
the original building, erected between 1863 and 1867. Scott's building forms the
three western blocks and consists of richly-arcaded and symmetrically-arranged
wings with a central porticoed entrance. Florence Nightingale acted as
consultant and many of her suggestions to improve nursing care were included.
No information has been traced about the source of the sandstone dressing for
this part of the Infirmary.

The wing to the east and three blocks to the rear were added in 1891–92 by
George Corson, following the original Scott design. Bolton Woods Stone,
Gaisby Rock (Coal Measures) from Bradford, was used for the sandstone
dressings of this extension. Dark Lake District 'Westmoreland' Slate, presumed
to be from the Burlington Quarries which work the blue-grey Upper Coldwell
Beds (Silurian), near Kirkby-in-Furness, Cumbria, cover the roof (*Building
News* 1889 p. 215). Beyond the Corson buildings are the noticeably very

FIGURE 13.   The General Infirmary, with St George's Church on the left

different 1930s extensions. The Brotherton Wing, which forms the Calverley Street frontage, is faced with Portland Stone (Walk 1:6).

Pillars are a feature of the arched ground floor windows and entrances. Polished red Peterhead granite was used for many of these, although Corson also included some pillars of a grey granite with small white feldspar crystals. The source of the latter rock has not been determined, but it is almost certainly not from Aberdeen. The pillars of the 1863 to 1867 buildings are some of the earliest examples of the use of granite in Leeds.

The two pillars on the corners of the Scott entrance portico are fine shafts of richly-crinoidal limestone. The stone is the variety known as Derby Fossil (Derbyshire Screws or Screw Stone) from the Carboniferous Limestone, once extensively quarried in the Monyash, Cromford and Wirksworth areas near Matlock in south-east Derbyshire. The deeply-weathered surface shows the details of the large-diameter crinoid stems, and the left-hand column has a marked vertical crack, indicating that the stone is edge-bedded (see Chapter 6). Derby Fossil is also used for the columns on the sides of the doorway, where the stone is very dirty, and through the entrance hall and staircase. The unweathered state of the internal columns should be compared with that of the portico columns which are exposed to the elements.

The two sandstone urns on the sides of the steps up to the main entrance are interesting relics of the Georgian stone heritage of Leeds. They were originally on the gateposts of the old Infirmary situated in Infirmary Street. The 1771 Infirmary was a relatively plain red-brick building with sandstone dressings. It was founded by Edwin Lascelles (Lord Harewood) who employed John Carr of York as architect. These two eminent men were completing Harewood House at this time, and it is interesting to speculate that the old Infirmary urns may have been 'surplus to requirements' at Harewood. If this is so, they will be of Lower Follifoot Grit (Millstone Grit), the medium-grained, rich-buff coloured sandstone from which Harewood was constructed (see 5:10).

5.7 Leeds Metropolitan University

Parts of the Leeds Metropolitan University, formerly the Leeds Polytechnic, are clad with two stones which are unusual in the way that they are used. Slabs of North Wales purple slate, with marked elongate green reduction spots, are used to clad the ground floors, and face-bedded (see Chapter 6), fine-grained, buff-coloured sandstone flags, possibly Elland Flags (Coal Measures), clad the upper floors. This paired cladding is well seen on the building at the corner of Calverley Street and Portland Way, opposite the side of the Civic Hall.

5.8 The Halifax (formerly The Leeds), Lovell Park Road (Figure 14)

A new Corporate headquarters for the Leeds Permanent Building Society was completed in 1992 on the north side of the Inner Ring Road between Lovell Park Road and Sheepscar Link Road. It was built in three phases, with R. A. Bromby and B. Binns, of Jones and Stocks, as architects.

Phases 1 and 2 (1989–91), at the Lovell Park Road end of the site, were constructed of red brick from Wakefield with medium-grained, buff-coloured sandstone for the string courses, sills, pier caps and corbel features, so creating a modern example of the Multicoloured Leeds style. When these parts of the complex were being planned, the construction industry was near one of its peaks, and difficulties were experienced obtaining supplies of sandstone. To ensure sufficient quantities for this contract, a disused quarry at Odda Hill,

FIGURE 14.   The Halifax, Phase 3 on the left, and Phase 1 on the right

Hawksworth, Guiseley, Leeds, was reopened, to work the Rough Rock Flags (Millstone Grit), from an area which produces good ashlar stone. A Swedish grey granite, Bohus Grey, was used to clad the plinth, with purple North Wales slates for the roof.

The walls of the Phase 3 building (1990–92), facing onto Sheepscar Link Road, are clad in sandstone with Bohus Grey granite string courses and plinth facings. The sandstone is from Stoke Hall Quarry, Grindleford (near Sheffield) in North Derbyshire where the Lower Kinderscout Grit (Millstone Grit) is worked. The roof is of purple North Wales slate.

The entrance foyers are clad in carefully-contrasting eye-catching coloured marbles, mostly from Spain and Portugal. The Phase 1 and 2 hall uses pale-pink Rose Aurora (walls and floors), dark-red Rosso Alicante (features, staircase treads and columns), grey Periwinkle (walls and borders) and small quantities of black Nero Marquina (margins). The Phase 3 building has a three-storey canopied foyer with dark-red Italian Breche Pernice (features), pale-pink Rose Aurora and grey Periwinkle (walls and flooring), and black Nero Marquina (margins). Details of the building are discussed in *Stone Industries* (Binns 1993, pp. 18–21), and the trade names of the decorative marbles are as recorded in this reference.

5.9 St Matthew's Church, Chapel Allerton (B)

In a sandstone city like Leeds, it is very surprising to find St Matthew's Church, Chapel Allerton, constructed entirely of buff-brown coloured Middle Jurassic oolitic limestone. Built in 1900 to the design of G. F. Bodley, the stones used were from Ancaster in Lincolnshire and Bath in Avon (*Building News* 1899, p. 6). Not only did the stone come from outside Yorkshire, but also workers from the Bristol area were employed on construction. The many parishioners with backgrounds in the local stone trades (the extensive Scott Hall quarries would still have been working) were very unhappy with this change in their fortunes, and it is said that some reacted by moving from St Matthew's to other local churches (Norman Mason of Chapel Allerton, personal communication 1993).

5.10 Harewood House (I, Plate 7b)

Harewood House is about 7 miles north of Leeds, on the A61 road to Harrogate, and is listed here because the sandstone from which it is constructed (the Lower Follifoot Grit, Millstone Grit), was subsequently used extensively in Leeds. It was built between 1759 and 1771 by Edwin Lascelles (Lord Harewood), to the design of John Carr of York with modifications by Robert Adams. From 1843 to 1850 the house was remodelled by Charles Barry (the architect of the Palace of Westminster), with the addition of a new top floor to the wings, a balustrade to the roof of the central block, remodelling of the south façade and the creation of the south-front terrace.

G

The Lower Follifoot Grit, a medium-grained, well-cemented, richly buff-coloured sandstone, was used for the exterior walls and locally-fired bricks for the interior walls. The stone for the 1771 building came from a line of quarries, possibly including Cockett's Quarry, on the north side of the Harewood to Stank road on the flank of the ridge overlooking the Wharfe valley. Not only was this source very close to the new building, but it had the additional advantages of producing high-quality, durable and beautiful stone which was admirable to work. Very good use was made of this excellent sandstone. Linstrum (1978, p. 74) remarked on the precision of the ashlar work and commented that 'the masonry of Harewood was meticulously detailed and executed. There is an almost mechanical perfection in the pattern of the chamfering of the rustication and in the practically invisible joints in the ashlar of the superstructure'. More than 200 years after it was built, much of the stonework is still as crisp as when it was fitted by John Muschamp and his team of a dozen local masons (Mauchline 1992; Kennedy 1982).

For the 1843 remodelling, the Lower Follifoot Grit from the original local quarries was used for much of the new stonework, which was fitted by the estate masons directed by master-mason Hope. In addition a second, darker, grey-weathering, coarse-grained sandstone was brought in for the balustrade on the roof and for parts of the south-terrace walling. The source of this stone may be the Caley Crags Grit (Millstone Grit), from Pool Bank Quarries. The grime of industrial Leeds was sand blasted off the exterior of the building in 1972–73.

The construction of Harewood House appears to have established the reputation of the Lower Follifoot Grit as a high-quality building stone. A new quarry was opened in the same Lower Follifoot Grit on Rawden Hill, about 1 mile west of the house, and worked by the firm of Trickett and Perkin from 1824 to 1859 (Leeds City Archives). Despite the problems and expense of carting the stone from Harewood, Rawden Hill sandstone was much used in Leeds and became one of the classic early-Victorian (1840s and 1850s) pre-railway sandstones of the city.

5.11 Merrion Centre Car Park

The exposed-aggregate panels of the Merrion Centre car park in Merrion Way are faced with a stone which is not used elsewhere in central Leeds. In their preparation, well-matched rounded cobbles of flint were carefully placed in rows in the bottoms of the moulds, onto which concrete was then poured. Before the concrete set it was washed off the flints, the result being a laudable attempt to improve the finish of a concrete building.

5.12 Schofields, The Headrow

The new Schofields Centre was built in 1987–88 to a design by Crampin and Pring. The building is in the Multicoloured Leeds style of red brick with buff-coloured sandstone dressings. The sandstone for the exterior and for the stone pilasters between the shops in the malls is Woodkirk Stone, Thornhill Rock (Coal Measures), from Britannia Quarries at Morley, Leeds. However, the pale-buff colour of the sandstone used for the exterior dressings is not typical of weathered Woodkirk Stone. The roofing uses Villar Del Rey Standard slates from Spain.

Beaumont and Cowling were the architects for the Schofields shop which forms The Headrow frontage of the Centre. Polished, generally buff-yellow coloured 30 cm square slabs of southern French and Italian 'marbles' (fine-grained limestones) were laid throughout for the floors and some walling, with a different variety on each floor. Level 1 has Jura Marble, Level 2 Clara Peach, Level 3 Perlatino Savino, Level 4 Diana, and Oniciato Marble between Levels 1 and 2.

5. 13 St John's Church, New Briggate (A, Figure 15)

St John's Church, the oldest stone building in central Leeds, was started in 1631 and consecrated in 1634. It was founded and endowed (1639) by John Harrison, a prominent merchant benefactor of the time. Woodhouse Stone, Elland Flags (Coal Measures), from the extensive medieval quarries on Woodhouse Moor, was used for the new church (Place 1945, p. 356), which was built in the fields outside the town on a rise once known as 'town cliff'. It is worth comparing the Victorian history of St John's with that of St Peter's Church in Kirkgate (see 5.20). Whereas the 1838 plans to enlarge and renovate St Peter's had to be

FIGURE 15. St John's Church

changed to demolition and a complete rebuild, the plans originally drawn up in the 1860s for the building of a new church on the site of St John's were changed to renovation. The architect R. N. Shaw, with support from George Gilbert Scott, objected to the demolition of St John's. Both men were convinced that St John's was not beyond repair, even though 'the walls were damp and there was external stone decay'. Their views, fortunately, prevailed.

Extensive renovation was carried out by Shaw between 1866 and 1868 but his work on the interior is now generally thought to have been too severe. Careful restoration of the internal carved woodwork, the outstanding feature of the original church, was undertaken after 1888 (Douglas and Powell undated, history of St John's Church).

Much of the exterior walling was repaired using a coarse-grained, grey-weathering, cross-bedded sandstone with conspicuous quartz pebbles, a stone that is probably the Rough Rock (Millstone Grit), although the source has not been determined. The pillars and arches of the nave are made of a buff-coloured, fine-grained sandstone which is presumably the original Woodhouse Stone.

The original stone slabs of the roof (likewise in poor condition in the 1860s) were also replaced. Scott recommended that Lake District green slates be used, but Shaw wanted Lake District blue slates. In the event reroofing took place in 1867 with 'Westmoreland' blue slate, presumably from the Upper Coldwell Beds (Silurian), in the Burlington Quarries, near Kirkby-in-Furness, Cumbria. New slates from Burlington Quarries were used when the church was again reroofed in 1995.

The floor of the church is laid with square marble slabs. Two colours are used, the pink ones being a Belgian marble, and the white ones with fine grey veins the Carrara marble variety known as Sicilian. The most memorable of the interior stones, however, are the ones used for the main door threshold, and for the steps from the nave up to the chancel. For these, blocks of the classic Frosterley Marble are used. This handsome stone is a dark-grey, almost black, fine-grained limestone crowded with eye-catching white fossil corals, and comes from the Great Limestone (Carboniferous Limestone). It has been worked extensively from the many quarries near Frosterley in the Stanhope area of Weardale, Co. Durham. Frosterley Marble has been used for many hundreds of years as an ornamental stone in churches, and particularly fine examples can be seen in Durham Cathedral. It was probably installed in St John's at the suggestion of George Gilbert Scott during the Victorian renovation (Dr G. A. L. Johnson, personal communication 1994). The finding of blocks of this distinctive stone in St John's was an exciting discovery; one of the gems of the rich building-stone heritage of Leeds. Frosterley Marble is also used in All Souls Church, Blackman Lane, built in 1876–80 as a memorial to W. F. Hook, the famous early-Victorian Vicar of Leeds. This church was designed by George Gilbert Scott shortly before his death (in 1878), and the font is a splendid example of the use of this classic British decorative stone. The pulpit has shafts of another long-used favourite, Purbeck Marble (Upper Jurassic), the distinctive dark-coloured limestone crowded with the shells of small freshwater gastropods.

St John's Church has been in the care of The Churches Conservation Trust since 1977.

5.14 Maples, Vicar Lane

Maples furniture shop in Vicar Lane, just north of The Headrow, is a red-brick building which has a most unusual and surprising green stone below the windows. It is Mountain Green (also known as Cold Spring Green, Aqua Pearl and Royal Emerald) and comes from Jay in the Adirondack Mountains of New York State, USA. This stone (of Precambrian age) is a fine- to medium-grained, green-coloured, pyroxene-garnet gneiss, a high-grade metamorphic rock of granitic appearance, with large pale-blue coloured iridescent feldspar porphyroblasts. Sold in the trade as a granite, Mountain Green is an unusual and eye-catching addition to the Leeds scene.

5.15 Holy Trinity Church, Boar Lane (A, Figure 16)

Holy Trinity Church in Boar Lane was built on ground where travelling theatres, circuses and the Leeds Fair were formerly held before it became an

FIGURE 16.   Holy Trinity Church

area of superior residences. The church was designed in 1722 by William Etty of York and was consecrated in 1727. The stone, referred to as 'Black Moor Stone' by Broadhead (1981, p. 29), is a coarse-grained, grey-weathering, cross-bedded sandstone with conspicuous quartz pebbles and is cut in very large blocks. Hopwood and Casperson (1986, p. 19) recorded that this sandstone came from the massive Meanwood Quarries in north Leeds where the Rough Rock (Millstone Grit) was worked. The stone was of the highest quality. Haulage of such large blocks would have been an expensive task. The distinctive 180-foot-high spire-like tower climbs in steps above the Leeds skyline. The three upper sections were designed and added in 1839 by R. D. Chantrell (the architect of the 1841 Parish Church), to replace the 1720s wooden spire damaged in the great storm of 7 January 1839. The tower, but not the main part of the church, was cleaned in about 1980.

The north end of the west façade of the 1982–83 Church Hall was built of Hawksworth Grit Stone, from the top beds of Hawksworth Quarry, Guiseley. It is a coarse-grained, grey-weathering sandstone with quartz pebbles, typical of the Rough Rock (Millstone Grit), and is an excellent match for the original stonework. The stone for the doorway and the wall above it came from the original hall, demolished in 1982. It is also Rough Rock sandstone. However, two of the urns on the roof of the church (at the south-west and north-east corners) were replaced in 1990 using sandstone from Blackhill Quarry, Kings Road, Bramhope, Leeds where the Brandon Grit (Millstone Grit), is worked. These urns are therefore made of a stone from a Millstone Grit horizon which is different from the Rough Rock of the original building. It will be interesting to see how they weather.

5.16 The Corn Exchange, Call Lane (I, Plate 8a)

The Corn Exchange in Call Lane, one of the finest mid-Victorian buildings in Britain, was the second of the massively-constructed buildings with which Cuthbert Brodrick made his reputation in Leeds (the others are the Town Hall (Walk 1:1) and the Mechanics' Institute (Walk 1:7)). It was built between 1861 and 1863. Early work, however, was delayed when excavations for the foundations, having removed about 4 feet of earth, uncovered 40 old ironstone bell-pits which were full of water and loose earth (*Builder* 1861, p. 651). This unusual elliptically-shaped building has been beautifully restored (1990). The interior with the off-centre glazing in its great domed roof is a remarkable and striking Victorian monument to the corn traders of Leeds. Suspended in the dome of the Corn Exchange is the Kitty Hawk Flyer, a working model of the Wright brothers aircraft in which the first successful human flight was made on 17 December 1903, at Kitty Hawk, North Carolina, USA.

The stonework of the whole building (walls, windows, surrounds, arches and porches) consists of rusticated blocks ornamented with unusual pyramid-shaped facets, and is cut with gently curved faces. The precision and sharpness of the blocks is a remarkable testament to the skills of the masons and to the high quality of the stone they worked. Coarse-grained, grey-weathering, cross-bedded sandstone with conspicuous quartz pebbles is used throughout. It is typical of the classic Rough Rock (Millstone Grit), but the many building-journal references of the time give no information about the quarry for the Corn Exchange stone. However, the use of Bramley Fall Quarry stone appears to have almost ceased after about 1839 (see Chapter 2), and it is possible that one of the Horsforth Rough Rock quarries with good rail links, such as the large Whitehall Quarry at Hawksworth, may have been the source. The paving of the ground floor is a fine example of the use of Yorkshire Flagstones — (the classic Elland Flags, Coal Measures).

5.17 TSB, Kirkgate

The present TSB building on the corner of Kirkgate and Vicar Lane was designed by William Bakewell for the London and Midland Bank. Opened in

1892, this modest building is nevertheless a fine example of the stone masons' craft. Stone for the façade was from Idle near Bradford, where the Gaisby Rock (Coal Measures) was formerly mined on a considerable scale, and from Morley where the Thornhill Rock (also Coal Measures) was quarried (*Builder* 1892, p. 146). The carvings which enrich the stonework were by J. W. Appleyard, the Leeds sculptor. The arms of London and Leeds are worked into the panel below the pediment, which is crowned by Midas flanked by two lambs, a lion and a unicorn, a mythical creature with deer's feet, a goat's beard, the tail of a lion and a single horn (now sadly missing). The statue of Midas provided the classic incentive to bank with the London and Midland. Midas was a king of Phrygia whose touch turned everything, including his daughter, into gold. He was given the ears of an ass by Apollo.

5.18 Leeds City (Kirkgate) Markets, Vicar Lane (II, Plate 8b)

The present Leeds City (Kirkgate) Markets, facing onto Vicar Lane, was built by Leeming and Leeming in 1903 to 1904. It is one of the finest market buildings in Britain, and continues the long tradition of covered markets in Leeds. The exterior is more richly modelled and carved than Bradford or Halifax markets. Extensive reconstruction of the interior was necessary after a serious fire in 1975. A major refurbishment, during which the southern dome was destroyed by fire, was finished in 1993.

Burt and Grady (1992) have published a history of Kirkgate Market and Mr S. Burt (personal communication 1992) has kindly supplied the following details from the Market Committee minute book for 8 August 1901. 'Resolution passed that in place of Holmfirth ashlar [sandstone] originally specified, stone from Radfield Quarries, Eccleshill, be used in the erection, and failing the supply of that stone in sufficient quantities, Idle Moor Stone be used. Mr Wright, builder, agreed to deduction from contract price of £695 16s 8d in respect of change of stone'; and for 19 August 1901: 'Tender of Messrs Thewlis and Co. for stone carvers' work for the new Market Hall accepted — sum of £3030 5s 0d'. This is the third example in Leeds of Thewlis' work. Radfield Quarries, Eccleshill (near Bradford) worked the Elland Flags (Coal Measures); Idle Moor, also near Bradford, mined Gaisby Rock (Coal Measures). The window surrounds for the shop fronts are clad in a mid-grey coloured variety of Larvikite, and replacement slabs show fresher and brighter colours.

5.19 Quarry House, Quarry Hill (Figure 17)

Quarry House, the heavily-criticized new headquarters for the Department of Social Security, was completed in 1993, the architects being the Building Design Partnership of Preston. The building complex is on a prominent site on Quarry Hill and dominates the eastern skyline of the city. It is another modern building in the Multicoloured Leeds style of red brick with sandstone dressings. Extensive use is made of a medium-grained, buff-coloured sandstone for the first floor cornice level, as a decorative feature within the brickwork above this level, and for the stone drum features to the main eastern elevation. This stone comes from Stanton Moor (Peak Moor Quarry), Stanton-in-the-Peak near Matlock, south-east Derbyshire, where the Ashover Grit (Millstone Grit) is worked.

FIGURE 17.   Quarry House

Two polished granites face the ground floor walls. Dark red Royal Mahogany from Sweden is used for the first metre above normal ground floor level, and pink Corrennie Granite from Aberdeen from this one-metre level up to the sandstone cornice at first floor level. The building is roofed with Westmorland blue slates, from the Lake District Upper Coldwell Beds (Silurian), worked in the massive Burlington Quarries near Kirkby-in-Furness, Cumbria.

The sandstone for the walls and paving of the landscaped gardens with their fountain, laid out to the west of Quarry House, is Woodkirk Stone, Thornhill Rock (Coal Measures), from Pawson's Britannia Quarry, Morley. When built in early 1993, it should be noted that some of this stone still showed its fresh grey colour (see comments about Morley Stone weathering and colour changes in Walk 3:57).

The sculptured central courtyards were created by Susan Tebby, but sadly are not open to public view because of security problems. They are of slabs of Lake District blue slate from the Burlington Quarries near Kirkby-in-Furness, and green slate from the Borrowdale Volcanic ashes of the Bursting Stone Quarry, Coniston, and the Elterwater Quarry in the Great Langdale valley.

5.20 *St Peter's Church, Kirkgate* (A, Figure 18)

Evidence suggests that there may have been five successive churches on or near this site since the seventh century, when Leeds was no more than a small village. The first building, probably of wood, may have been the one which Bede said was burnt down in about A.D. 633. The second was the Anglo-Saxon church mentioned in the Domesday Survey of 1086. The third was early Norman, the main evidence for which is that Norman stonework was reused in the fourteenth-century church. The much larger fourth church, demolished in 1838 to make way for the present building, was partly fourteenth-century, with considerable sixteenth-century replacement and repair following the destruction of much of the earlier choir by a fire in about 1500. There is little evidence regarding the stone that was used for this pre-1838 parish church. All that appears to remain of the old church are the old font and the piscina canopy which is now used for the Thoresby Monument. Both of these are made of fine-grained, buff-coloured, Coal Measures sandstones. With the heavy costs of carting stone in early days, the source may not have been far away. Quarries on Quarry Hill are unlikely to have been used. This area is underlain by an unnamed sandstone in the Coal Measures, above the Elland Flags, consisting mainly of fine-grained, strongly-laminated, buff-coloured sandstone with thin layers of plant debris. This would not have made a very durable building stone. The extensive medieval stone quarries on Woodhouse Moor which worked Elland Flags (Coal Measures), are a possible source, but it is emphasized that no documentary evidence exists for this suggestion.

In 1837 W. F. Hook became Vicar of Leeds. He realized that many repairs and alterations were needed. The architect R. D. Chantrell was appointed originally to enlarge and renovate the existing building, but when much of the

FIGURE 18.   St Peter's Church

old structure was found to be more unsound than was at first thought and beyond repair, plans were agreed for its demolition and for the construction of a new church (Moore 1877, p. 6).

The present building was opened in 1841, and Moore (1877, p. 9) recorded that the exterior stone was from Bramley Fall and other sandstone quarries in the neighbourhood, one of which was at Horsforth (Eastwood in *Builder* 1901, p. 490). The walls are made of large blocks of coarse-grained sandstone with quartz pebbles and cross-bedding, a stone which is consistent with the Rough Rock (Millstone Grit) from that area. The freestones for the columns of the interior were from 'Gipton, Weardly and other quarries'. Gipton refers to quarries north-east of Harehills, later referred to as Harehills Quarries where the Elland Flags (Coal Measures) were worked; Weardly is a hamlet about 1 mile west of Harewood, where the Lower Follifoot Grit was quarried on Rawden Hill by Trickett and Perkin from 1824 to 1859 (Leeds City Archives). Rawden Hill to the Parish Church was a long way to have carted stone in 1838, suggesting that the sandstone from this quarry was either of very high quality or had some other advantage (such as patronage of Lord Harewood).

Much of St Peter's Church was reroofed in 1996. The old North Wales purple slates were replaced with new ones of similar colour from Penrhyn, near Bangor. However, the old slates on the inner (north) side of the south aisle roof, which cannot be seen from street level, have been retained. They are Lake

District blue slates, from the Upper Coldwell Beds (Silurian), in the Burlington Quarries, near Kirkby-in Furness, Cumbria.

Accounts of the long history of the Leeds Parish Church of St Peter have been given (amongst others) by Moore (1877), who had been a pupil of R. D. Chantrell, the architect appointed to demolish the old church and to construct the present building (1838–41); and by Sprittles (undated guide).

5.21 Anglian Crosses

The recovery of fragments of Anglian crosses in Leeds, and of the travels of the Church (or Leeds) Cross before it was erected within the present St Peter's Church in 1880, makes a fascinating story (McGuire and Clark 1987). These important relics, together with much other old stone work, had been built into the tower of the medieval church. Fortunately when this building was being demolished in 1838, the architect R. D. Chantrell recognized the significance of

these carved stones and was able to save a number of them. The Church Cross, positioned near the altar in St Peter's Church, is the most complete of the crosses. However, there are doubts about the correctness of the carving of some of the new stones added by Chantrell, and the wheel-head stone at the top of the shaft is thought to belong to another cross. Six other stones are in the Leeds City Museum and, in all, remains from at least five crosses have been preserved. All the stones are of a coarse-grained, grey-weathering sandstone from the Millstone Grit. Without obvious quartz pebbles, the stone is not the Rough Rock.

The Leeds Crosses are Anglian with some Scandinavian influence and are dated to the tenth century. They have artistic links with other remains from Wharfedale, such as the Collingham, Otley and Ilkley Crosses. It may be that all these Anglian monuments are from a single source or workshop, possibly near Otley where coarse-grained Millstone Grit is the common rock type.

In early Christian times crosses were preaching centres, but after churches were established, they were used for

Reconstruction drawing of the Church Cross by P. Brears

memorials to mark the graves of local lords and their families. Sculptured stones from what may have been a group of crosses suggest, therefore, that a significant settlement existed around the site of the parish church in the ninth and tenth centuries. The remains of these Anglian crosses are the oldest surviving relics of the building-stone heritage of Leeds.

5.22 Bar Stones

There were at least four Bar Stones which marked the medieval boundary between the manorial borough of Leeds and Leeds Main Riding, the surrounding agricultural land. They do not imply any form of fortified gateway or entrance.

The Burley Bar Stone (or West Bar) was situated at the western end of Upperhead Row, on the south side, immediately to the west of where Albion Street joins the present Headrow (Heap 1990; Cossins 1725 Plan). This stone, now preserved within the Albion Street office of the Leeds and Holbeck Building Society (see Walk 4:88), is a block of fine-grained, buff-coloured Coal Measures sandstone which may have come from the medieval stone quarries on Woodhouse Moor, where Elland Flags (Coal Measures) were worked.

The East Bar (or York Bar) is in the churchyard wall of St Peter's Church, east of the Memorial Cross, facing onto Kirkgate (Sprittles 1969, p. 89; Cossins 1725 Plan). It is made of a coarse-grained, grey-buff coloured sandstone with quartz pebbles and is probably a block of Rough Rock (Millstone Grit). The fact that it is made of the same stone as the 1841 St Peter's Church makes it possible that it was replaced during the building of the new Parish Church. The Rough Rock for the new church (5.20) came from the Bramley Fall area in the Aire valley near Kirkstall; this stone would not have been readily available in Leeds during medieval times.

The North Bar is built into the shop-front brickwork on the east side of Vicar Lane just north of the Lady Lane junction, but in 1993 was covered by the green-painted woodwork of a new amusement arcade. It is another block of fine-grained, buff-coloured Coal Measures sandstone.

A fourth stone, marking the Leeds–Hunslet boundary, was recorded by Sprittles (1969, p. 89) as being on the corner of Junction Street at the Hunslet Lane end of Great Wilson Street. This could not be found in 1991, and has either been preserved elsewhere or swept away during the extensive road widening and redevelopment that has taken place in this area.

5.23 Windsor House, Sovereign Quay

Windsor House faces onto Bridge End and the River Aire, immediately north of Leeds Bridge. It is built of red brick with sandstone dressings and has been refurbished (1994) as part of the Sovereign Quay Development. Restoration of the stonework included ten new hand-carved Ionic column capitals supplied by Johnsons Wellfield Quarries, Huddersfield, using their Crosland Hill Stone, the atypically finer-grained Rough Rock (Millstone Grit). Each of their stone masons was given the task of carving one capital. The supporting columns have also been reclad in new slabs of smooth-dressed Crosland Hill Stone. They rest on plinths faced with a pale-pink coloured granite known as Giallo Veneziano from South America. The surface of this stone has a sandblasted finish. Windsor House has an important place in history, because the building featured in what was probably the world's first successful moving-picture film, 'Leeds Bridge', made in 1888 by Louis Le Prince, a Yorkshire-based Frenchman. The Aire and Calder Navigation building on the south side of Leeds Bridge, from which this film was taken, saw another earlier event of significance. It was here in 1847 that the 'Band of Hope' movement was founded, the title being suggested by the Reverend Jabez Tunnicliffe, a prominent Leeds temperance worker.

CHAPTER 6

Detailed Classification of Rocks

As discussed in Chapter 3, any rock making up the Earth's crust can be placed into one of three big groups: igneous, sedimentary and metamorphic. This is the fundamental classification. However, within these groups many varieties exist, and it is possible to subdivide igneous rocks, for instance, depending on a number of critical factors within that group. Thus detailed classifications may be erected, founded on geological principles. The stone trade, however, does not observe these restrictions and frequently uses names in a different way, 'granite', for example, being used for any igneous rock — indeed for some rocks which are not igneous! Similarly 'marble' is used in the stone trade for any calcareous rock (whether true marble or compact limestone) and even serpentinite, which can be cut and polished. The names given in the text are generally those supplied by the architect who will have obtained them from the stone trade. Where it is known, the correct geological name is also included. The modern worldwide explosion in decorative-stone production has led to the coining of many new names such as 'Periwinkle' (a Portuguese marble), and the pirating of others (for example 'Bon Accord' and 'Juparana') for stones from sources far distant from the original and even of quite different lithologies.

The classifications given here are based on geological principles. Readers wishing to pursue the subject of rock description and classification further, should refer to the Geological Society of London Handbook Series; on igneous rocks (Thorpe and Brown 1985), on sedimentary rocks (Tucker 1982), and on metamorphic rocks (Fry 1984).

Igneous Rocks

Igneous rocks are formed from initially molten material. Those that are extruded at the Earth's surface as a result of volcanic activity are fine grained, or have no grain at all, because they were cooled very rapidly. Igneous rocks that resulted from the slow cooling of molten rock, deep within the Earth's crust, are coarse grained. Thus a classification can be based on position of emplacement.

However, that classification takes no account of the chemical composition of the rock melts, which differ widely. It is possible to classify igneous rocks on the basis of their chemistry, usually by determining the proportion of silica (silicon dioxide; SiO_2) present in the rock. Rocks with a high percentage of SiO_2 are termed *acid*. Those with a low percentage are *basic* or even *ultra-basic*. It is important to distinguish between silica (SiO_2), and the element silicon (Si), used widely in electronic components (chips).

The simplified classification given here combines both emplacement and chemistry as the basis of division.

Those igneous rocks which have been used as building stones in Leeds are shown in **BOLD** type.

Position of Emplacement	Chemical Composition			
	High Proportion of SiO_2			Low Proportion of SiO_2
	Acid	Intermediate	Basic	Ultra-Basic
Extrusive or volcanic rocks (glassy or very fine grained)	Pumice Obsidian Rhyolite	Andesite Trachyte	Basalt	
Minor intrusions — close to surface (fine grained or medium grained)	Quartz-porphyry	Porphyry	Dolerite	
Plutonic or deep seated rocks (medium grained or coarse grained)	**Granodiorite** **Granite**	**Diorite** Syenite	**Gabbro**	Serpentinite

Sedimentary Rocks

Sedimentary rocks are the result of the breakdown, weathering and erosion of pre-existing rocks. The erosion products are transported and deposited elsewhere as sediments, usually in water, later to be lithified and thus to become sedimentary rocks. In great part, therefore, the nature of sedimentary rocks depends on the source material.

A unique and fundamental characteristic of sedimentary rocks is that they are *bedded*; that is, the erosion debris is deposited in layers along which the stone will often split easily. The presence of fossils is another indication that the rock is a sediment.

The basic classification given here (see table on p. 84) distinguishes between detrital (fragmental) sediments, chemical deposits and organic deposits. Grain size is the primary feature used to classify detrital sediments.

Sedimentary rocks that are found in Leeds buildings are shown in **BOLD** type.

Metamorphic Rocks

A wide variety of metamorphic rocks exist, reflecting the many different types of rock which make up the Earth's crust, and the great heat and pressure to

Rock Type	Name	Main Constituents	Remarks
Rudaceous (rubbly rock, of large fragments)	Breccia	Large fragments of any rock type	The fragments are *angular*
	Conglomerate	Large fragments of any rock type	The fragments are *rounded*
Arenaceous (sandy)	**Sandstone**	Quartz grains	The grains are *rounded*
	Grit(Stone)	Quartz grains	The grains are *angular*
	Flagstone	Quartz grains and mica flakes	Finely bedded with mica lying along the bedding planes
	Arkose	Quartz grains with feldspar	A sandstone with over 25% feldspar
	Quartzite	Quartz grains	Closely fitting quartz grains, naturally cemented with silica
Argillaceous *(clayey)	Clay*	Clay mud	Very fine grained, flakey minerals, structureless
	Mudstone	Clay mud	Clay, with water squeezed out, fine grained, structureless
	Shale	Clay mud	Laminated, compacted mudstone
Calcareous (Carbonate rocks)	**Limestone**	Calcium carbonate	Bedded, organic or chemical
	Oolitic Limestone	Ooliths of calcium carbonate	Mostly of small spherical 'ooliths'
	Magnesian Limestone	The carbonates of magnesium and calcium	A limestone with a high proportion of dolomite
	Travertine	Calcium carbonate	A carbonate rock deposited from lime-rich warm water
Organic	Peat	Organic remains	Unconsolidated
	Lignite	Organic remains	Partly consolidated
	Coal	Organic remains	Consolidated
*Chemical** precipitates*	**Chert & Flint**	Silicon dioxide with greater or lesser amounts of impurities	

---

*   Clay is the essential primary material for brick and tile making.
**   There is controversy about the origin of chert and flint. They are included here for convenience.

which these have sometimes been subjected. Many complicated classifications may be erected.

The simplified one given here is based on the nature of the original rock and the type of metamorphism to which it was subjected. The two types of metamorphism are dynamo-thermal, found on a regional basis in mountain-building (orogenic) belts, and contact or thermal, found near igneous intrusions. Those metamorphic rocks seen in Leeds buildings are shown in **BOLD** type.

ROCK TYPE AND ORIGIN (SEDIMENTS)	TYPE OF METAMORPHISM DYNAMO-THERMAL			CONTACT
	Low grade	Medium grade	High grade	
Pelitic rocks: from argillaceous (muddy) sediments	**Slate**	**Schist**	**Gneiss**	Hornfels
Psammitic rocks: from arenaceous (sandy) sediments	Quartz-grit	**Quartzite**	**Quartzite**	**Quartzite**
Calcareous rocks: from calcareous sediments (i.e. limestones)	**Marble**	**Marble**	**Marble**	Marble

IGNEOUS ROCKS give rise to **Schist** or **Gneiss**

Problems with Stone

BEDDING OF SEDIMENTARY ROCKS

Sedimentary rocks were originally laid down as a succession of layers of sediment. The plane separating one layer, or bed, from the next in the sequence is known as the bedding plane. Beds, bedding and bedding planes are unique features of sedimentary rocks. Bedding is essentially more-or-less horizontal, although cross-bedding or dune-bedding may be produced in particular conditions. A block of stone taken from a quarry, therefore, can be placed in one of three attitudes into a building; in-bed, edge-bedded or face-bedded. When used in a building, a sedimentary rock should be placed so that the thrust on the stone is at right angles to the plane of the bedding.

ASSOCIATIVE DECAY

Many of the buildings in Leeds rely for their architectural impact on a variety of different stones. The different textures and colours of the stones provide the visual interest. However, not all stones may be used together without regard to their nature. Particularly, care must be taken when limestone and sandstone are used in the same building. If a limestone is placed physically above a sandstone, the sandstone may eventually disrupt.

H

Limestone is made up mainly of calcium carbonate ($CaCO_3$). Rainwater contains carbon dioxide (CO_2) and is thus slightly acid; in recent times, pollution has increased this acidity due to a rise in the CO_2 level (and to sulphur dioxide; SO_2). When rain water containing CO_2 falls onto a limestone surface, some calcium carbonate is taken into solution in the form of calcium bicarbonate ($Ca(HCO_3)_2$). When the water washes down onto a sandstone beneath, it saturates the accessible surface pores. As the water evaporates, calcium carbonate is redeposited in the pores of the sandstone. Eventually, after repeated cycles of saturation, evaporation and re-deposition of calcium carbonate, the grains of the sandstone are forced apart. The disruption of the sandstone may take some considerable time, depending on factors such as the type of limestone, the porosity of the sandstone and the architectural detailing.

An example of this process can be seen outside the Town Hall (1858; Walk 1:1) where the Rough Rock (Bramley Fall Stone), a particularly strong engineering sandstone, is being disrupted by the lime-rich water from the limestone of the Portland Stone lions. However, on St Anne's Roman Catholic Cathedral (1904; Walk 1:11), it is interesting to observe that the Horsforth Stone, also Rough Rock (Millstone Grit), has not yet been disrupted by wash from the Ketton Stone, an oolitic limestone.

SULPHATION

Many limestone surfaces present a rather dirty-looking yellowish appearance. Almost certainly this will be the result of a process known as sulphation. Unfortunately, the air of today contains a significant proportion of sulphur dioxide (SO_2). This oxidizes and reacts with the calcium carbonate ($CaCO_3$) of the limestone to produce calcium sulphate ($CaSO_4.2H_2O$; that is, in mineralogical terms, gypsum). Thus, a thin skin is formed on the limestone surface, which holds dirt and leads to the discoloration. It may be noted here that great care must be exercised when cleaning sulphated surfaces.

RISING DAMP

On some buildings in Leeds, for example the Norwich Union entrance (Walk 3:46), it may be seen that the stone of the lower courses is disrupted. This is caused by the process known as rising damp or as rising salts. Unless the stone of the building is isolated from the earth on which it stands, the stone acts rather like a wick, and damp is drawn up by capillary action. This ground water will contain many salts — such as sulphates, nitrates and chlorides. When the saturated stone of the building dries out, these salts are deposited in the pores and thus the stone is disrupted.

Three zones may be distinguished. At the base, a saturated zone, in which the stone is continuously wet and no effect is seen. Above that is an active zone, which is alternately wetted and dried. It is here that the stone is disrupted. Commonly, a white salt deposit may be seen. Above the active zone is the dry zone, into which the water is not drawn up, and no disruption is seen.

ACKNOWLEDGEMENTS

Many people with detailed knowledge of various aspects of the building stones and history of Leeds have given us great help and encouragement during the preparation of this work. Our thanks go to: The staff of the Art Library and Local History Library who provided ready access to reference material, particularly *The Builder* and *The Building News* journals; Mr John Ayers who introduced us to Mr John Roberts with whom we had many long discussions about quarrying and the history of the use of stone in the area; Messrs S. Barton and J. H. Bowles of The Churches Conservation Trust for information about St John's Church; Mr Iain Burgess for invaluable help with the local geology and the details of Millstone Grit and Coal Measures sandstones; Mr Steve Burt for information about St John's Church and the Kirkgate Market; Mrs Ann Clark for help with the history of St Peter's Church; Messrs Paul Davison, Ian Duncan and John Varker who kindly gave us personal notes made on building stone walks round central Leeds led by the late Professor Versey in 1953 and 1974; Mr R. E. Finnigan, the Assistant Diocesan Archivist, who checked and improved our St Anne's Roman Catholic Cathedral section; Mr Alan Garlick of Abbey House Museum for information about Burmantofts and terracotta buildings; Miss Sally Gordon and Mr Albert Hodgkinson who checked the Harewood House section and provided helpful information; Dr Kevin Grady, Director of the Leeds Civic Trust, who kindly helped with our brief account of the history of Leeds; Miss Melanie Hall for details of the sculptor Joseph Thewlis; Professor Derek Linstrum who discussed aspects of our study; Mr Steve Moorhouse for information about medieval stone quarrying in Leeds; Mr Richard Taylor, Principal Conservation Officer, Department of Planning, Leeds City Council, and Mrs Susan Wrathmell who helped with information about the Listed Buildings of Leeds; officers of the Department of Planning for answering numerous enquiries; Mr Robin Sanderson who reported on the petrography of some of the more unusual stones, so helping us with their identification; Mr Robin Shackleton who, when on 'work experience' at the City Museum, made valuable searches in the Archives and through building journals; Dr Susan Tebby for the information about the stones used for the Quarry House courtyard sculptures; and Mr C. A. Ussher, Agent for the Harewood Estate who allowed access to the site of Rawden Hill Quarry which is now filled in. Our very special thanks goes to Mr Keith Denton who willingly gave of his considerable knowledge and interest in Leeds building stones, gained during a long career with Andrews of Meanwood, — the Shop Fronts Walk benefited enormously from his cheerful help.

Typing of early drafts of parts of the text was undertaken by Mrs Gill Philipson of the City Museum and Mrs Jane Howard of Kingston Vale. However, the major task of word processing, altering and correcting the script was most cheerfully carried out by Miss Lesley Enoch of the Department of

H*

Earth Sciences, University of Leeds whose efforts are gratefully acknowledged. The sketches, except for that of the Church Cross, have been drawn by Miss Vanessa Warnes and the maps by Mr Jerry Hodgson, both of whom are thanked for their major contributions. The Church Cross sketch is reproduced from McGuire and Clark (1987) with permission of Mr P. Brears. The black and white photographs were printed by Mr D. Bailey of the University of Leeds Photographic Section; the support of the Department of Earth Sciences for this work is acknowledged. The colour plates are from Kodachrome transparencies taken by Murray Mitchell. Map 1 is based on the British Geological Survey Ten Mile Map with permission of the Director; NERC copyright reserved.

The following architects, contractors, masonry consultants and quarry managers have supplied valuable information. Their forbearance with requests for help is gratefully acknowledged: Mr G. Akesson Abiat (David Lyons and Associates); Mr D. P. Baxter (Leach Rhodes Walker); Mr D. Boyes (Abbey Hanson Rowe); Mr R. A. Bromby (Jones and Stocks); Mr M. Brook (Marshalls Mono); Messrs R. Bull and K. G. Varley (Lloyds Bank); Messrs D. J. Bye and K. McHale (John Brunton Partnership); Mr I. Campbell (BLC); Mr A. V. Carter (Costain Management Design); (Chapman Taylor Partners); Mr M. Clayton (D. J. Curtis and Associates); Mr R. Cornfield (Leeds Design Consultancy); Messrs R. H. Cropper and P. Barker (Leeds and Holbeck Building Society); Mr R. Cowling (Beaumont and Cowling); Mr D. J. L. Denbigh (Waterhouse Denbigh's Bolton Woods Quarry, Bradford); Mr R. M. Elsdon (Building Design Partnership); Miss E. Fecitt (Kirkstone Quarries, Cumbria); Miss K. Fell and Mr H. Ogden (Burlington Slate Quarries, Cumbria); Miss H. Ferrett (Natural Stone Products, De Lank, Bodmin, Cornwall); Messrs A. Gascoigne and D. Senior (Pawson's Britannia Quarries, Morley); Mr D. Gillson (Naylor Hill Quarry, Haworth); Mr E. Green (Midland Bank Archivist); Mr G. Heptonstall (Hawksworth Quarry, Odda Hill, Guiseley); Mr S. Hodgkinson (Derek Latham); Messrs C. Jones and J. Wilson (Carey Jones); Mr P. Juniper (A. Andrews and Sons, Marbles and Tiles); Mr B. S. Kidd (Laing North East); Mr B. B. Karia (Laithwaite and Ward); Mr C. Knight (William Gower and Partners); Mr A. Lingorski (Polarstone Marble and Granite); Mr D. E. Lodge (Johnsons Wellfield Crosland Hill Quarries, Huddersfield); Mr J. Lyall (John Lyall); Mr R. C. Mason (Cobban and Lironi); Mr J. W. Maud (The Rushbond Group); Mr M. R. Metcalfe (D. G. S. Jesper Stone Cladding); Mr M. Milburn (Laing Masonry); Messrs P. and K. Mone (Blackhill Quarry, Bramhope); Mr J. Moran (Jeremy Dixon, Edward Jones, BDP); Mr A. Potts (Plumb Bespoke Shopfitting); Mr R. Rawson (former owner of Apex Quarry, Horsforth); Mr C. Sewell (Kitson and Partners); Mr A. Sheard (Peter Kilmartin and Partners); Mr K. Sheridan (NJSR); Mr H. M. Smith (Fletcher Joseph); Mr J. W. Smith (J. W. Smith Masonry); Mr D. Swarbrick (Crampin and Pring); Mr D. Walker (Derek Walker Associates); Mr J. Wignall (Cumbria Stone, Cumbria); Mr J. R. Wilson (Shaws of Darwen); Mr C. Wood (Terry Farrell); and Mr B. Woodhams (James Thorp and Partners).

To anyone who helped us with this work but has been unintentionally omitted from the list, our apologies and thanks.

REFERENCES

There are many references to the use of building stone in Leeds in *The Builder* (from Volume 1 published in 1843, to 1966; continues from 1967 as *Building*), and *The Building News* (from Volume 1 published in 1855, to 1926; from 1926 combined with *The Architect* as *Architect and Building News*; and from 1971 continued as *The Architect*).

BARRY, C. (1839) *The selection of stone for the building of the new Houses of Parliament.* Report to the Commissioners of Her Majesty's Woods etc.

BEDE. *Historia Ecclesiastica.* Edited by Plummer 1896.

BERESFORD, M. (1988) East End, West End: the face of Leeds during urbanisation, 1684–1842. *Publications of the Thoresby Society* 60 & 61 for 1985 and 1986: 1–562.

BINNS, B. (1993) New home for The Leeds. *Stone Industries* (April 1993): 18–21.

BRADFORD ART GALLERIES & MUSEUMS, & LEEDS CITY MUSEUMS. (1984) *Burmantofts Pottery.* Leeds.

BRIGGS, A. (1961) The building of Leeds Town Hall: A study in Victorian civic pride. *Publications of the Thoresby Society* 46 (3): 275–302.

BROADHEAD, I. E. (1981) *Exploring Leeds. A guided tour.* Tetradon, Warley.

BURGESS, I. C. & COOPER, A. H. (1980) The Farnham (I.G.S.) Borehole near Knaresborough, North Yorkshire. *Report of the Institute of Geological Sciences* (80/1): 12–17.

BURT, S. & GRADY, K. (1992) *Kirkgate Market: An illustrated history.* Leeds.

CLARKE, P. (1989) *Jubilee 150. The story of St George's Leeds.* Leeds.

DEXTER, W. (1925) *The England of Dickens.* Cecil Palmer, London.

DICTIONARY OF ARCHITECTURE. (1848–92) Architectural Publications Society, London. Issued in parts: plates 1848–52, text 1853–92.

DIMES, F. G. (1988) Napoleon Marble. *Stone Industries* (March 1988): 21–25.

DOUGLAS, J. & POWELL, K. (1988) *Leeds: Three architectural walks.* Victorian Society Walks No. 4, Leeds. 2nd Edn.

DOUGLAS, J. & POWELL, K. (Undated) *St John's Church, Leeds. A history.* Redundant Churches Fund, London.

EDWARDS, W., MITCHELL, G. H. & WHITEHEAD, T. H. (1950) Geology of the district north and east of Leeds. *Memoir of the Geological Survey of Great Britain*, Sheet 70.

EDWARDS, W., WRAY, D. A. & MITCHELL, G. H. (1940) Geology of the country around Wakefield. *Memoir of the Geological Survey of Great Britain*, Sheet 78.

FRY, N. (1984) The field description of Metamorphic Rocks. *Geological Society of London, Handbook Series.*

GODWIN, C. G. (1984) Mining in the Elland Flags: a forgotten Yorkshire industry. *Report of the British Geological Survey* (84/4): 1–17.

GOSDEN, P. H. J. H. & TAYLOR, A. J., eds. (1975) *Studies in the history of a University 1874–1974: To commemorate the Centenary of the University of Leeds.* Arnolds, Leeds.

GRADY, K. (1989) The Georgian public buildings of Leeds and the West Riding. *Publications of the Thoresby Society* 62 (133): 1–192.

HEAP, A. (1988) *Briggate: A history in pictures.* Leeds City Libraries.

HEAP, A. (1990) *The Headrow: A pictorial record.* Leeds City Libraries.

HOPWOOD, W. A. & CASPERSON, F. P. (1986) *Meanwood.* Leeds.

IRWIN, W. & BRANSON, F. W. (1926) *Yorkshire stones from quarries.* Pp. 260–265 in Handbook of the Old Leeds Exhibition, held in the City Art Gallery July 8th–23rd 1926. Gardham, Leeds.

KENDALL, P. F. & WROOT, H. E. (1924) *Geology of Yorkshire: An illustration of the evolution of Northern England.* Vienna. Two volumes.

KENNEDY, C. (1982) *Harewood: The life and times of an English country house.* Hutchinson, London.

LAKE, R. D., NORTHMORE, K. J., DEAN, M. T. & TRAGHEIM, D. G. (1992) Leeds: A geological background for planning and development. *British Geological Survey Technical Report* WA/92/1.

LINSTRUM, D. (1969) *Historic Arcitecture of Leeds*. Oriel, Newcastle upon Tyne.

LINSTRUM, D. (1978) *West Yorkshire Architects and Architecture*. Lund Humphries, London.

MCGUIRE, A. & CLARK, A. (1987) *The Leeds Crosses*. Leeds City Museums.

MAUCHLINE, M. (1992) *Harewood House: One of the treasure houses of Britain*. Moorland, Ashbourne. 2nd Edn.

MODERN BUILDING RECORD in 5 Volumes: 1 (1910), 2 (1911), 3 (1912), 4 (1913) and 5 (1914).

MOORE, R. W. (1877) *A history of the Parish Church of Leeds from the earliest known period down to the present time*. Rivingtons, London.

MYERS, L. (1972) Granite faced bank. *Stone Industries* (September/October 1972): 11–14.

PLACE, J. B. (1945) Woodhouse in the Manor of Leeds. *Publications of the Thoresby Society* 37 (4): 345–65.

PLUMMER (1896) see BEDE.

POOL, S. (1972) Quartzite — elegant by any name. *Stone Industries* (September/October 1972): 16–22.

SPRITTLES, J. (1969) Links with bygone Leeds. *Publications of the Thoresby Society* 52 (115): 1–124.

SPRITTLES, J. (undated) *Leeds Parish Church: history and guide*. Cheltenham.

STEPHENS, J. V., MITCHELL, G. H. & EDWARDS, W. (1953) Geology of the country between Bradford and Skipton. *Memoir of the Geological Survey of Great Britain*, Sheet 69.

THORESBY, R. (1715) *Ducatus Leodiensis*.

THORPE, R. S. & BROWN, G. C. (1985) The field description of Igneous Rocks. *Geological Society of London, Handbook Series*.

TUCKER, M. E. (1982) The field description of Sedimentary Rocks. *Geological Society of London, Handbook Series*,

VERSEY, H. C. (1940) Ornamental stones of Leeds. *Transactions of the Leeds Geological Association* 5 (5): 297–300.

WATERS, C. N., AITKENHEAD, N., JONES, N. S. & CHISHOLM, J. I. (1996) Late Carboniferous stratigraphy and sedimentology of the Bradford area, and its implications for the regional geology of Northern England. *Proceedings of the Yorkshire Geological Society* 51 (2).

WATSON, J. (1911) *British and foreign building stones: a descriptive catalogue of the specimens in the Sedgwick Museum, Cambridge*. Cambridge University Press.

WRAY, D. A., STEPHENS, J. V., EDWARDS, W. & BROMEHEAD, C. E. N. (1930) Geology of the country around Huddersfield and Halifax. *Memoir of the Geological Survey of Great Britain*, Sheet 77.

GLOSSARY

ALGAE — a diverse group of primitive plants ranging from unicellular forms to sea-weeds, and occurring from the Precambrian to the present day

AMMONITE — a now-extinct fossil of the group Cephalopoda, having a chambered shell commonly coiled in a plane spiral. Distantly related to the present day Nautilus and octopus

ARCADE — a row of arches supported on free-standing columns

ARRIS — sharp edge formed by the meeting of two surfaces

ASHLAR — large blocks (usually) of stone with flat even faces and square edges fixed in regular courses to build walls of buildings

AUGITE — a type of pyroxene (q.v.)

BALUSTRADE — row of small pillars or balusters supporting a coping

BAR (stone) — a Leeds term for a stone set up to mark the boundary between the town of Leeds and the surrounding country. The equivalent of a boundary stone

BED, BEDDING — a roughly horizontal layer (bed) of sedimentary rock. Individual beds are separated by bedding planes

BELL PITS — pits dug vertically to reach a mineral deposit, so named from the shape, wider at the bottom than at the top

BIOTITE — a mineral of the mica group (q.v.), widely found in igneous rocks. It appears dark brown or black in hand specimens

BOASTED — a finish on a stone surface produced by a mallet and a chisel ('boaster') to give parallel bands across the surface

BORROWDALE VOLCANIC GROUP — volcanic rocks of Ordovician age which crop out in the Lake District. An important component is the green-coloured slates which were originally fine-grained volcanic ashes

BRACHIOPOD — a marine animal of two shells of unequal size held together either by muscle, or by muscle and a hinge structure; equilateral but not equivalved. Belongs to the Phylum Brachiopoda

BRECCIA, -TED — a rock of angular fragments, normally coarse grained, cemented into a fine-grained matrix. The fragments are of other rock-types.

BURGAGE (plot) — a plot of land in a city for which a yearly rent was paid to the landlord

BUTTRESS — a mass of masonry built against a wall to strengthen it

CALCAREOUS — containing calcium carbonate ($CaCO_3$)

CALCITE — the commonest crystalline form of calcium carbonate ($CaCO_3$), usually white or grey; the chief constituent of limestone and of marble

CAPITAL — the top part of a column

CARBONIFEROUS — a division of the Palaeozoic era. Subdivided into three parts; the Carboniferous Limestone, the Millstone Grit and the Coal Measures. (see Table 1)

CARBONIFEROUS LIMESTONE — see Carboniferous

CHANCEL — the eastern part of a church containing the altar

CHERT — a dense, hard crypocrystalline form of silica (SiO_2), occurring in nodules, occasionally bands, generally in limestones. The purest form, found in the Chalk, is known as flint

CHLORITE, -IC — a group of minerals, generally greenish in colour, mostly of hydrated silicates of aluminium, iron and magnesium

COLONNADE — a row of columns

COLUMN — a round pillar supporting some part of a building

CORAL — an attached marine animal, of the Class Anthozoa, often with a calcareous skeleton. Typically of warm seas. Common as fossils

CORBEL — a block projecting from a wall, usually supporting another architectural feature

CRETACEOUS — a division of the Mesozoic era. (see Table 1)

CRINOID — an important rock-forming marine fossil with a jointed stem of circular plates (columnals), belonging to the Phylum Echinoderma

CROSS BEDDED, -ING — oblique bedding (of sedimentary rocks) indicating original deposition on a sloping structure such as a dune or delta

CUPOLA — a small dome (or rounded roof with a circular base)

DELF 'OLE — a local Yorkshire dialect name for a small quarry

DERBY FOSSIL — see Derbyshire Screws

DERBYSHIRE SCREWS — a dialect name for fossil crinoid columnals found in the Carboniferous Limestone, particularly in Derbyshire. Also known as Derby Fossil or Screw Stone

DIORITE — a dark-coloured, coarse-grained, plutonic rock, with chemistry intermediate between granite and gabbro; consisting mostly of hornblende, augite and plagioclase feldspar

DOLOMITE — a mineral, the double carbonate of calcium and magnesium ($CaMg(CO_3)_2$), commonly found in limestone, hence dolomitic limestone. The term 'dolomite' is also used for rocks composed wholly of the mineral dolomite

DOLOMITIC LIMESTONE — a limestone containing a significant amount of the mineral dolomite (q.v.)

DRESSINGS — an architectural term for stone worked to a finished surface and used decoratively around door openings, windows and other features

EDGE-BEDDED — a block of stone laid with the natural bedding-surface in a vertical plane at right angles to the face of a building (see also Bed, Bedding, Face-bedded and In-bed)

ELLAND FLAGS — a series of sandstones with siltstones and mudstones within the Lower Coal Measures. They may be easily split into thin slabs for use as paving stones (flags)

ENTASIS — a slight convex curve used on columns to prevent the optical illusion of concavity

FACE-BEDDED — a block of stone laid with the natural bedding-surface in a vertical plane parallel with the face of a building (see also Bed, Bedding, Edge-bedded and In-bed)

FAIENCE — a term for glazed earthenware or porcelain. From the Italian town of Faenza

FAULT — a fracture in the rocks of the earth's crust, along which rocks on one side have been displaced relatively to the other either vertically, horizontally, or both

FELDSPAR — a group of rock-forming alumino-silicate minerals, important constituent minerals in igneous rocks. The two main varieties are plagioclase (containing Na, Ca and Al), and orthoclase/microcline (containing K and Al)

FERROMAGNESIAN MINERALS — a portmanteau name for a group of typically dark- coloured silicate minerals containing iron and magnesium, common in igneous rocks

FIRECLAY — a clay with a high proportion of silica that withstands high temperatures without disintegrating. Widely used to make firebricks

FLAGS, -STONE(S) — a sedimentary rock, usually sandstone, that may be split parallel with the bedding and used for paving (flags). From Viking flaggstone — a flat stone

FLINT — a pure form of chert (q.v.) only occurring as nodules in the Chalk. Note that overseas the name flint is used for most chert deposits

FLOW BANDING — banding resulting from flow movements in viscous magma, the flow lines shown by bands of different mineral composition aligned roughly parallel

FRIEZE — decorated band, usually at the top of a wall or building

GABBRO — a dark-coloured coarse-grained basic plutonic rock, mostly of plagioclase feldspar and pyroxene, sometimes with olivine or hornblende

GARNET — a ferromagnesian mineral group with great chemical variation. Found particularly in metamorphic rocks; pink or red in colour

GASTROPOD — a mollusc of the Class Gastropoda. With a single shell, usually coiled, closed at the apex

GEOPETAL — a cavity within a fossil partly filled with sediment (now consolidated) which preserves the original bedding orientation of the sediment

GNEISS — a coarsely crystalline, foliated ('banded') metamorphic rock, the folia being discontinuous

GRANITE — a coarse-grained acid plutonic igneous rock consisting essentially of sodic and potassic feldspar, mica and quartz

GRANODIORITE — a coarse-grained plutonic igneous rock with mineralogy intermediate between granite and diorite

GYPSUM — a mineral, hydrated calcium sulphate ($CaSO_4.2H_2O$). The massive fine-grained variety is known as alabaster

HORIZON — a layer of sediment at a particular level in a sequence of beds

HORNBLENDE — a complex group of ferromagnesian minerals found in igneous and metamorphic rocks, dark brown, dark green or black in colour

IGNEOUS (rocks) — one of the three main groups of rocks making up the earth's crust. These rocks have cooled and consolidated from magma (q.v.)

IN-BED or ON-BED — a block of stone laid with the bedding planes in a horizontal plane (see Bed, Bedding, Edge-bedded and Face-bedded)

IRONSTONE — a sedimentary rock rich in iron minerals

JURASSIC — a division of the Mesozoic era. (see Table 1)

KARST — a type of topography, typically developed in limestone areas, of crisscross widened joints enlarged by water solution. The scale may vary from a few cms upto several thousand metres (e.g. Kwelin, in China)

LARVIKITE — a particular variety of syenite (q.v.). Named after the town of Larvik on Oslofjord, Norway

LIMESTONE — a sedimentary rock composed principally of calcium carbonate ($CaCO_3$)

MAGMA — a fluid melt of rock material, highly charged with gases (mainly superheated steam), and generated deep within the earth's crust: the source of igneous rocks

MAGNESIAN LIMESTONE - i) a limestone containing a high proportion of magnesium carbonate; ii) a division of the Permian

MAGNETITE — a mineral, an oxide of iron $(Fe,Mg)Fe_2O_4$, which is magnetic; common in some igneous rocks

MARBLE — in strict definition, a fine- to coarse-grained metamorphic rock arising from the complete recrystallization by metamorphism of limestone. In the stone trade the name is commonly used for any calcareous (and some other) rocks that can be cut and polished

METAMORPHIC — one of the three main groups of rocks making up the earth's crust. These rocks have been formed by the alteration of pre-existing rocks by heat or pressure within the crust

MICA — a group of silicate minerals characterized by platy habit and perfect basal cleavage, and containing K, Mg, Fe and Al. Common in some igneous and metamorphic rocks

MINARETS — slender ornamented turrets

MONOLITH -IC — a large single stone, normally used for a column or a free-standing monument

NEW RED SANDSTONE — a general portmanteau term for rocks of Permo-Triassic age

OOLITH(S) — small spheres of concentrically-deposited calcium carbonate $(CaCO_3)$, usually around a nucleus of a sand grain or shell fragment. The main constituent of oolitic limestones

OOLITIC LIMESTONE — a limestone composed of ooliths (q.v.)

OPHICALCITE — a rock, normally a marble, which contains a significant amount of the mineral serpentine (q.v.) arising from the metamorphism of a dolomite-rich limestone

ORDOVICIAN — a division of the Palaeozoic era. (see Table 1)

ORTHOCERAS — a fossil cephalopod having a straight, slightly tapered, chambered shell

OXIDISATION — process of combining with oxygen

PEDIMENT — a low-pitched triangular gable above a door or window

PERMIAN — a division of the Palaeozoic era. (see Table 1)

PILASTER — a part column or shallow pier attached to a wall

PINNACLE — small ornamental tapering turret, usually crowning a buttress or roof

PISCINA — a basin for washing the communion or mass vessels, set generally in the wall to the south of the altar

PLASTIC (MORTAR) REPAIR — a mortar mix which may include stone dust, made to resemble the surrounding stonework and which can be moulded when in a plastic state to the original profiles of the building

PLINTH — projecting base of a wall or column

PLUTONIC — a term applied to major intrusions of igneous rock, formed deep beneath the surface of the earth. Generally coarsely crystalline

PORPHYROBLAST — a large crystal, formed during metamorphism, in a metamorphic rock

PORTICO — the roofed entrance to a building, usually forming the centre piece of the façade

PYROXENE — a group of ferromagnesian minerals, containing iron, magnesium, calcium and sometimes sodium and potassium

QUARRY SAP — a quarry term for the moisture present in a recently quarried block of stone

QUARTZ — a mineral, consisting of silica, i.e. silicon dioxide (SiO_2). A very important rock forming mineral

QUARTZITE — i) a sandstone of quartz gains naturally cemented by silica; ii) a metamorphic rock of tightly interlocking quartz grains formed by the metamorphism of a sandstone

QUOINS — dressed stones used at the corners of buildings

RAPAKIVI STRUCTURE — the structure exhibited by feldspars in some granites. Large, somewhat rounded, corroded feldspar crystals surrounded by a reaction rim of a soda-rich plagioclase feldspar

REACTION RIM — the zone around a mineral grain of other mineral matter resulting from the reaction of the earlier crystallized mineral with the magma

REDUCTION SPOTS — coloured spots, commonly 'green', seen on the surface of slate, and caused by the reduction (chemical depletion in oxygen) of iron minerals. Usually elongated

REVEALS — the side surfaces of a recessed door or window

RISING SALTS — water with contained soluble mineral matter (salts) moving by capillary action up a stone (or other) wall which, when the water evaporates, deposits the salts on the surface of the stone. syn. RISING DAMP

ROCK-FACED — the rough 'natural looking' finish on the surface of a worked stone, to show no tool marks

RUBBED — stone which has been finely dressed on the face by abrasion with another stone

RUSTICATION — blocks of stone, usually used at plinth course levels, with a margin cut back to give V-shaped joints between the blocks

SACCAROIDAL — the weathered surface of marbles resembling the surface appearance of sugar loaves; a granular texture

SANDSTONE — a sedimentary rock made up principally of grains of the mineral quartz (q.v.)

SCHIST — a metamorphic rock in which the minerals have a parallel alignment (schistosity) along which the rock splits easily

SCREW STONE — see Derbyshire Screws

SEASON -ED, -ING — the process of letting newly quarried blocks of stone stand for some time before use to allow the quarry sap (q.v.) to evaporate

SEDIMENTARY (rocks) — a rock formed by the consolidation of sediments originally laid down on the floors of seas and lakes, or on land surfaces

SERPENTINE — a group of rock forming minerals, consisting of hydrated magnesium/ iron silicates

SERPENTINITE — a rock made up mostly of the mineral serpentine (q.v.)

SHAFT — column between plinth and capital

SILICA — silicon dioxide (SiO_2), forming the mineral quartz, and more rarely chert or flint

SILURIAN — a division of the Palaeozoic era. (see Table 1)

SLATE — a fine-grained metamorphic rock arising from the dynamic metamorphism of argillaceous (muddy) sediments, or less commonly volcanic ashes, displaying facile cleavage along planes independent of original bedding

STOPPED — a stone in which natural voids and cavities are filled with a mixture of stone dust and cementing material. Also known as filling or waxing

STOPS — stones, commonly carved or protruding, defining the bottom ends of arches (hood-mould, dripstone, label)

STRING COURSE — projecting horizontal band set in a wall

STROMATOLITE — a blue-green alga with a calcareous base. Fossil stromatolites usually appear as roughly laminated calcareous masses

STYLOLITE — a plane, usually roughly parallel with the bedding, found in limestones, along which pressure solution has occurred leaving an irregular line of insoluable material of contrasting colour to the host rock

SULPHATION — the change of a limestone surface ($CaCO_3$) to a skin of calcium sulphate ($CaSO_4.2H_2O$) by the chemical interaction of sulphur dioxide (SO_2) and oxygen in slightly acid rain with the limestone

SURBASE — large blocks of stone forming layer above the plinth

SYENITE — a coarse-grained, plutonic igneous rock, with chemistry intermediate between granite and gabbro, but with less hornblende & augite and more plagioclase & potassic feldspar than diorite

TERRACOTTA — literally, 'burnt earth': hard earthenware tiles used as a building material

TERTIARY — a division of the Caenozoic era. (see Table 1)

THACKSTONE — a dialect word for a heavy slab, usually of sandstone, used for roofing

THIN SECTION — a slice of rock, typically 30µm thick, mounted on a glass slide so that it may be studied microscopically

TRAVERTINE — a calcium-carbonate deposit formed by precipitation from warm lime-rich waters

VENETIAN WINDOWS — with three separate openings, the central one being arched and bigger. Common in England in the seventeenth and eighteenth centuries

VERMICULATED — a surface of irregular ridges looking like 'worm tracks' imposed on the face of a stone

WEATHERING — the breakdown of rocks by the action of the natural agencies (rain, snow, frost, water)

XENOLITH — a fragment of a pre-existing rock in an igneous rock. Known by stone workers as 'foreigner' or 'heathen'

I

APPENDIX

Names of buildings in date order (1850 to 1911)

The text-references are to where the buildings are described in Chapter 4, Walks 1–4 (W2:20) and in Chapter 5 (Ch.5.16)

TEXT REFERENCE	DATES	BUILDING STREET	ARCHITECT	MATERIALS
W4:69	1852–55	Moorlands House, Albion Street	W. B. Gingell	Sandstones from Bramley Fall, Pool Bank & Rawden Hill
W1:1	1853–58	Town Hall, The Headrow	C. Brodrick	Sandstones from Bramley Fall, Calverley Wood, Pool Bank, Rawden Hill & Derbyshire
Ch.5.16	1861–63	Corn Exchange, Call Lane	C. Brodrick	Local sandstone
W2:38	1862–64	Sovereign House, Park Row	P. C. Hardwick	Ringby sandstone & Scottish granite
W3:61	1863	Hepper House, East Parade	G. Corson	Harehills sandstone, Scottish granite & serpentinite
Ch.5.6	1863–67	General Infirmary, Great George Street	G. G. Scott	Brick with sandstone dressings & Scottish granite
W1:7	1865–68	Mechanics' Institute, Cookridge Street	C. Brodrick	Horsforth sandstone

W2:19	1869	St Andrews Chambers, Park Row	G. Corson	Local sandstones & Scottish granites
W1:3	1876–84	Municipal Buildings, Calverley Street	G. Corson	Bolton Woods sandstone, Shap & Scottish granites
W3:54	1878	St Paul's House, St Paul's Street	T. Ambler	Brick & Doultons Terracotta
W1:4	1878–81	School Board Building, Calverley Street	G. Corson	Sandstones from Pool Bank & Burley-in-Wharfedale
Ch.5.4	1880	Textile Buildings, University, College Road	A. Waterhouse	Brick with Spinkwell sandstone dressings
W1:8	1885	Coliseum, Cookridge Street	W. Bakewell	Morley sandstone
W1:16	1887–88	Art Gallery, Centenary Street	W. H. Thorp	Bolton Woods sandstone
W1:9	1889	City of Leeds School, Woodhouse Lane	Kelly & Birchall	Brick with sandstone dressings
W3:47	1890	Liberal Club, Quebec Street	Chorley & Connon	Brick & Terracotta from Ruabon
Ch.5.6	1891–92	General Infirmary extension, Great George Street	G. Corson	Brick with Bolton Woods sandstone dressings & granites
W2:31	1892	Woolwich Building Society, Park Row	Smith & Tweedale	Bolton Woods sandstone & Scottish granite
Ch.5.17	1892	TSB, Kirkgate	W. Bakewell	Sandstones from Idle and Morley

The text-references are to where the buildings are described in Chapter 4, Walks 1–4 (W2:20) and in Chapter 5 (Ch.5.16)

TEXT REFERENCE	DATES	BUILDING STREET	ARCHITECT	MATERIALS
Ch.5.4.6	1893–94	Old Medical School, Thoresby Place	W. H. Thorp	Brick with Morley sandstone dressings
W3:57	1894	Yorkshire (Penny) Bank, Infirmary Street	G. B. Bulmer	Morley sandstone
Ch.5.4.1	1894	Great Hall of Yorkshire College, College Road	A. Waterhouse	Brick with Bolton Woods sandstone dressings
W2:20	1894	Prudential Building, Park Row	A. Waterhouse	Burmantofts Faience & Scottish granite
W3:45	1896	Post Office, City Square	H. Tanner	Haworth sandstone, with Shap & Scottish granites
W1:2	1896–1903	Methodist Chapel, Oxford Place	G. F. Danby & W. H. Thorp	Brick with Morley sandstone dressings
W3:51	1897–98	Metropole Hotel, King Street	Chorley & Connon	Brick & Terracotta from Ruabon
W2:33	1898	Greek Street Chambers, Park Row	A. Waterhouse	Burmantofts Faience & Scottish granites
W4:80	1898–1900	County & Cross Arcades, Briggate & Vicar Lane	F. Matcham	Burmantofts Faience
W3:60	1899	East Parade Chambers, East Parade	—	Burmantofts Faience

W 3:41	1899	Observatory, Bishopgate	W. W. Gwyther	Bolton Woods sandstone & Scottish granites
Ch. 5.9	1900	St Matthew's Church, Chapel Allerton	G. F. Bodley	Bath & Ancaster stone
W 1:13	1900	Masonic Hall, Great George Street	J. M. Bottomley	Brick with red Corncockle sandstone dressings
W 1:10	1900	Pupil Teachers' Centre, Great George Street	J. M. Bottomley	Brick with sandstone dressings
W 2:21	1900	Abtech House, Park Row	Oliver & Dodgshun	Huddersfield sandstone & Scandinavian granites
W 1:11	1902–04	St Anne's RC Cathedral, Cookridge Street	J. H. Eastwood & S. K. Greenslade	Horsforth sandstone & Ketton stone
Ch. 5.18	1903–04	Kirkgate Market(s), Vicar Lane	Leeming & Leeming	Eccleshill sandstone
W 3:56	1905	Goodbard House, King Street	–	Local sandstone
Ch. 5.4.5	1908–28	Adult Education Centre, Springfield Mount	Temple Moore	Brick with Pool Bank sandstone dressings
W 2:37	1909	Scottish Union & National Ins. Co., Park Row	Perkin & Bulmer	Burmantofts Marmo Faience
W 3:52	1910	Atlas Chambers, King Street	Perkin & Bulmer	Burmantofts Marmo Faience
W 3:67	1911	Pearl Chambers, The Headrow	W. Bakewell	Portland stone & Scottish granite

Index of Stones by Name

Index of Buildings

Names of buildings arranged alphabetically (or by street and number). Numbers in *italic* indicate pages where figures occur; those in **bold** refer to plates.

General Index